Journeys

Direct Instruction Reading

Level 2

Textbook 2

Siegfried Engelmann

Owen Engelmann

Karen Lou Seitz Davis

Ann Arbogast

SRA

A Division of The McGraw·Hill Companies

Columbus, Ohio

Illustration Credits

Shirley Beckes, Dave Blanchette, Dan Clifford, Olivia Cole, Mark Corcoran, Susanne DeMarco, John Edwards and Associates, Len Epstein, Meryl Henderson, Susan Jerde, Steph Pershing, Jan Pyk, Charlie Shaw, Jim Shough, Lauren Simeone, Joel Snyder, Karen Tafoya, and Gary Undercuffler.

SRA/McGraw-Hill

A Division of The McGraw·Hill Companies

Printed in the United States of America.

Send all inquiries to:
SRA/McGraw-Hill
250 Old Wilson Bridge Road, Suite 310
Worthington, OH 43085

ISBN 0-02-683535-5

1 2 3 4 5 6 7 8 9 VHJ 03 02 01 00 99

ai   ar   ay

1. <u>wonder</u>ing
2. <u>reaching</u>
3. help<u>less</u>
4. when<u>ever</u>
5. a<u>cross</u>

1. children
2. number
3. merry
4. happy

1. streak
2. m<u>ou</u>th
3. spends
4. weak
5. park
6. paint

1. music
2. fen<u>ce</u>
3. ra<u>ce</u>
4. strong
5. th<u>ou</u>ght

Sweetie and the Bird Bath
Part Three

Sweetie hated water, and he was all wet.

Sweetie's ears went back, and he shot out of that bird bath so fast that he looked like a yellow streak. He darted out of Bonnie's yard and back into his yard.

Then he hid under his h<u>ou</u>se. He had his m<u>ou</u>th open, and his eyes were very wide.

"What happened?" he said to himself. "One second I was reaching out for a little bird, and the next second I was getting slammed into the water."

Sweetie wasn't looking at the bird bath. He never saw the eagle. And while Sweetie was hiding under his h<u>ou</u>se, the eagle left. As soon as the eagle left, all the little birds returned to the bird bath.

At last, Sweetie came out from under his h<u>ou</u>se and looked at the bird bath. He saw the same little birds he saw before. Sweetie looked at those birds for a long time. Then he said to himself, "From here, those birds look pretty small and weak. But when you get close to them, they are really big and strong. I don't think I'll ever go near that bird bath again."

So now Bonnie is happy because her bird bath always has a lot of pretty birds in it. The birds are also happy because they can meet all their pals and have a bath whenever they want. The only one who is not happy is Sweetie. Sweetie spends a lot of time looking at the birds in Bonnie's yard, but he never goes over there. Sweetie also spends a lot of time wondering how those birds can look so small and weak, but be so big and strong.

The end.

Scott had a kitten that went up a tree. Scott went up the tree to get the kitten down. He went very high in the tree. But Scott got stuck.

He called for help, and after a while, a cop came. The cop went up into the tree to get Scott down. The cop went so high he got stuck, too. At last a fireman came with a long ladder. The fireman set up the ladder against the tree. Scott and his kitten and the cop came down. When Scott was on the ground, he told the fireman, "Thank you."

1. Where did Scott's kitten go?

2. Did Scott try to get the kitten down?

3. Who got stuck trying to get Scott down?

4. Who got them down?

1. Rolla
2. merry-go-round
3. music
4. children
5. racing
6. number

1. <u>for</u>ward
2. un<u>hap</u>py
3. <u>quick</u>er
4. <u>on</u>to
5. <u>thro</u>wn

1. hardly
2. closely
3. dizzy
4. jumpy

1. work
2. world
3. worst
4. mothers

Rolla
Part One

There once was a wonderful merry-go-round in a park. Everybody liked that merry-go-round. The music would play, and the horses on the merry-go-round would go up and down with children on them. The music was good. The horses were pretty. So the mothers were happy, and the children were happy.

Almost all the horses were happy. But one horse was not happy at all. That horse was named Rolla. She was not happy because she had a big 8 painted on her side. There were only 8 horses in the merry-go-round, and she was horse 8. So she thought she was in last place.

As she went up and down, she kept thinking, "Why should I be horse 8? Why can't I be horse 5 or horse 3?" She was as big as the other horses. She went just as fast as they did. So why couldn't she have a better number?

The more she thought about it, the more she thought she would like to be number 1. That would be the best number a horse could have. But how could she get a better number?

For days she thought about it. Then she said to herself, "The only way I can get a better number is to go faster. If I pass up the horse in front of me, I'll be horse number 7, and that horse will be horse 8. If I pass up all the other horses, I'll be number 1."

More next time.

front   of   back

Ted was lazy. He didn't work ar<u>ou</u>nd the h<u>ou</u>se. Ted didn't do anything. One day, Ted's mother told Ted, "If you don't do work ar<u>ou</u>nd <u>ou</u>r h<u>ou</u>se, you'll have to go live somewhere else."

Ted asked, "What kind of work do I have to do to stay here?"

His mother handed him a list. So Ted mo<u>w</u>ed the l<u>aw</u>n, washed the dishes, and cleaned the flo<u>or</u>. Now Ted does the work on the list his mother gives him every day.

1. If Ted didn't work around his house, he would have to live ▆▆▆▆ .

2. Ted's mother gave him a ▆▆▆▆ .

3. Write the things Ted did.
   - mo<u>w</u>ed the l<u>aw</u>n
   - washed dishes
   - washed the car
   - cleaned windo<u>w</u>s
   - cleaned the flo<u>or</u>
   - made beds

4. Now what does Ted do every day?
   - plays
   - sleeps
   - works
   - rests

1. dizzy
2. jumpy
3. closely
4. hardly

1. poles
2. swing
3. bunch
4. fixed
5. quicker

1. worst
2. world
3. worked
4. wondered

1. right
2. different
3. whispered
4. racing
5. forward
6. nodding

Rolla
Part Two

Rolla was horse number 8, but she wanted to become horse number 1. She knew that there were 8 horses on the merry-go-round. So she'd have to pass up all the other horses. She didn't know that her plan couldn't work.

On the next day, she tried to pass up the other horses. And she tried very hard. She started to go faster. She went up and down quicker, and she went forward faster. But when Rolla went faster, all the other horses had to speed up, too. Even the music had to go faster.

That fast merry-go-round did not make the mothers or the children happy. The horses were going up and down so quickly that the children could hardly hang onto them.

The merry-go-round was turning around too fast for the mothers to stand next to their children. The mothers had to hang onto the poles to keep from being thrown off. But they went so fast that their feet went flying in the air. When the merry-go-round stopped, everybody was dizzy.

One mother got off the merry-go-round and said, "This is the worst merry-go-round in the world. Even the music is jumpy and bad."

The horses on the merry-go-round didn't like it any better than the mothers did. They were getting sore and tired from jumping up and down and racing like the wind. They kept yelling at Rolla, "Slow down. This is not fun." But all day, she kept trying to pass up the horse in front of her. But she couldn't do it.

And at the end of the day, she was as sore and tired as the other horses.

More next time.

hole	small

Jim told all his pals, "I like to hike. I can hike up any trail there is." He walked up and down three steep trails. Then he came to a very big hill. He hiked up the trail for a long time. He did not reach the top of that hill. When he came back, he complained. Jim said, "I don't like to hike very much after all."

1. At first, who liked to hike?

2. Did he reach the top of the hill?

3. Does he like to hike now?

1. howl
2. nut
3. shake
4. drop
5. write
6. different

1. ice
2. right
3. high
4. eye
5. wood

1. apples
2. follows
3. whispering
4. suddenly
5. fixed
6. bunch

1. dog
2. summers
3. sometimes
4. painting

Haw, haw.

Rolla thinks she's in last pla<u>ce</u>.

Rolla
Part Three

Rolla was tired and very sad. "I'm tired of being number 8," she told the other horses. She had a tear in her eye. "But I can't seem to pass up the horse in front of me."

"Is that your problem?" horse number 1 asked. "Do you think your number shows that you are in last pla<u>ce</u>?"

All the horses gave her a big horse laugh.

Horse number 3 said, "Numbers don't mean anything. Every horse follows another horse, and every horse is right in front of another horse."

"Yes," horse number 5 said. "If you look behind you, you'll see horse number 1. So you are really in front of all the other horses."

But Rolla didn't believe this. After they talked and talked, she still said, "But I'm number 8, so I must be the last horse on this merry-go-round." She had another big tear in her eye.

The other horses whispered to each other and nodded their heads up and down. They had a plan. After some more whispering and nodding, horse number 2 said, "Rolla, if you had a different number, would you stop trying to go fast?"

"Yes, yes," she said.

The horses worked hard painting and fixing things up to make everybody happy.

So if you go to Rolla's merry-go-round today, you won't hear any mothers complaining about the music or about horses racing around and around. You won't see children who are scared. You won't see mothers hanging onto poles as hard as they can. You'll see a happy bunch of horses going around at a good speed. You'll hear music that is pretty and not jumpy. You'll see children laughing and mothers smiling. You'll also see that the horses are smiling. And if you look very closely, you'll see that one horse has a bigger smile than the other horses. That horse is number 1, and her name is Rolla.

The end.

Today it rained. It started in the morning before the sun came up, and it rained until after it was dark. It was raining when I woke up. It was raining when I went to bed. The sun didn't shine all day. They say that it will not rain for another week.

1. All day long it ▉▉▉▉.

2. When did it start raining?

3. Did the sun shine at all?

4. Will it rain the day after next?

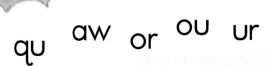

1. st<u>oo</u>d
2. wood
3. chop
4. drop
5. star~~e~~
6. share

1. evening
2. <u>ic</u>e
3. apple
4. shak~~e~~
5. nuts
6. wag

1. <u>s</u>uddenly
2. <u>h</u>owling
3. <u>s</u>ometimes
4. <u>out</u>side

1. put
2. cloth~~e~~s
3. dog
4. cook

Waldo and the Hungry Dog
Part One

Waldo was an old man who was very poor. He lived by himself in a small h<u>ou</u>se that was near a forest. There was a lake that was about a mile from Waldo's h<u>ou</u>se.

In the summer, W<u>a</u>ldo liked to walk to the lake and fish. He liked the hot sun. Summers were good for W<u>a</u>ldo, because there was a lot of food around. There were apples and nuts growing on trees. There were other things he could pick and eat. So W<u>a</u>ldo was never hungry in the summer time.

But winter was no fun for Waldo. He would always run low on food before spring came. He would even run out of wood for his fire. There was lots of wood in the forest, but that wood was under three feet of snow. There were nuts on the ground, but the nuts were under three feet of snow.

There were lots of fish in the lake, but there was snow on the lake, and below the snow was ice. To get fish, Waldo had to clear the snow away and then chop a hole in the ice. Waldo would drop his fishing line into the water and wait for a fish. Sometimes, he would have to wait a long time before he got one. Sometimes, the wind would howl, and the cold air would make Waldo shake.

More next time.

filled   pail   woman

A crow saw a nut on the ground. The crow said, "I think I'll eat that nut." So the crow grabbed the nut and started to fly away with it.

Just then the nut said, "Set me down. Set me down."

The crow dropped the nut and said, "I never saw a talking nut before."

A bug came out of the nut and said, "I am not a talking nut. I am a talking bug. This nut is my home."

1. Who saw the nut on the ground?

2. What did the crow want to do with the nut?

3. What was inside the nut?

4. The bug told the crow that the nut was his ▇▇▇.

1. ab<u>le</u>
2. tab<u>le</u>
3. <u>even</u>ing
4. <u>out</u>side

1. woman
2. put
3. suddenly
4. dream

1. <u>dress</u>ed
2. <u>cook</u>ed
3. <u>pat</u>ted
4. <u>clear</u>ed

1. plate
2. stared
3. flash
4. chopped
5. clothes
6. howl

1. warm
2. bed
3. dog
4. share
5. wag

Waldo and the Hungry Dog
Part Two

One year was very bad for Waldo. He got sick in the fall and did not pick very many apples and nuts. Winter started suddenly, with a cold wind and lots of snow. Soon Waldo was low on wood for his fire and had only two apples. He said to himself, "I'll have to get some fish from the lake."

So Waldo put on lots of clothes and hiked to the lake. He cleared the snow and chopped a hole in the ice.

He fished most of the day. But he got only
three small fish. He said to himself, "These fish
won't make a very good meal." Then he hiked
back to his house. On the way, he saw a big dog
near the forest. The dog looked very thin.

That evening, Waldo cooked the three fish. He set out one of his apples, and he was just sitting down to eat.

Suddenly, a howling sound came from outside. At first, Waldo believed that it was the wind. The howling sound came again. So Waldo got up and opened the do<u>or</u>. There was the big dog that Waldo had seen before. The dog stared at Waldo with a sad look, and then the dog's tail started to wag.

Waldo said, "You look cold and hungry. Come in. It is not as cold in here."

The dog came inside.

"You poor dog," Waldo said. "I wish I had food to share with you. But all I have is three small fish."

The dog wagged her tail again.

More to come.

A dog and a cat played with a ball of string. They were in the front yard of their house. The cat held one end of the string. The dog ran with the ball of string. The dog ran around and around the yard. The ball of string got smaller and smaller as the dog ran around. Soon there was no ball of string, but there was a mess in the front yard.

1. Who held one end of the string?

2. Who ran with the ball of string?

3. Did the ball of string get bigger or smaller?

4. What did the front yard look like?

1. quiet**ly**
2. quick**ly**
3. pat**ted**
4. shari**ng**
5. dress**ed**

1. door
2. floor
3. able
4. table

1. friend
2. person
3. woman
4. alone

1. bed
2. dogs
3. warm
4. put

1. dinner
2. plate
3. dream
4. flash
5. wagging

This will keep you warm.

Waldo and the Hungry Dog
Part Three

Waldo let a big, thin dog into his house.

Before Waldo started to eat, he took an old coat and put it on the floor. "This will keep you warm," he said to the dog.

Waldo patted the dog. Then he sat down at the table to eat. He looked at the dog. The dog did not howl or cry. The dog just stared at him, and Waldo could see that the dog was very hungry.

Waldo looked at the three fish. Then he looked at the dog again. He said to himself, "I can not eat without sharing what I have." Then he said, "Come over here and have one of my fish."

The dog sat next to Waldo, and Waldo gave a fish to the dog. The dog ate it quickly. Waldo started to eat a fish. The dog sat quietly and watched him eat. Waldo ate the fish slowly. Then he looked at the last fish and said to the dog, "You need this more than I do." And he gave his last fish to the dog.

All at once, the dog turned into a pretty woman dressed in white. She said, "You are a very good man, Waldo. You were hungry, but you gave me most of what you had. So from this day on, you will never be hungry or cold again."

Then there was a flash, and Waldo was all alone in his house. He was sitting on his bed. He said, "It must have been a dream."

This is not the end.

baked

The fox still had some bitter butter. He saw Gorman and said to himself, "I'll bet I can talk Gorman into trading me something for this butter."

The fox asked Gorman, "What will you trade me for this sweet, sweet butter?"

Gorman was not fooled. The turtles had told everyone about the bitter butter. So Gorman said, "If you let me have that butter, I will let you take a row boat out on the lake."

The fox said, "I like row boats."

So the fox went rowing in the boat. But when he came back, he was not happy. He was all wet.

The fox said, "I hate toads who sink boats."

1. Did the fox want to trade the butter or sell the butter?

2. What did Gorman let the fox do?
   • ride a horse   • sail a boat   • row a boat

3. When the fox came back, he was ▓▓▓▓.
   • dry   • wet   • happy

4. Who sank the boat?

ur

aw

ch

ou

qu

1. thou**ght**
2. bou**ght**
3. ri**ght**
4. ni**ght**

1. <u>i</u><u>ce</u>
2. <u>c</u>ent
3. la<u>ce</u>
4. pla<u>ce</u>

1. yeah
2. worm
3. fur
4. spent
5. stamp
6. contest

1. smil<u>ing</u>
2. dream<u>ed</u>
3. bel<u>iev</u>e
4. shout<u>ing</u>

1. friend
2. heard
3. person
4. dinner
5. glad

40

Waldo and the Hungry Dog
Part Four

Waldo was sitting on his bed. He thought he had dreamed about the dog and the woman. He got up and said, "I will eat my dinner now."

He looked where he kept his apples, but he did not see two old apples. He saw a pile of big, sweet apples. "What is this?" he said. "Who put these apples here?"

He picked up an apple and went to where his three small fish were. But he did not see three small fish. He saw three very big fish. "I can not believe what I see," he said.

41

Just then, he heard a sound at the door. He opened the door. In the snow was the dog, but now the dog was not thin and hungry. The dog seemed to be smiling as she looked at him.

"Come in, my friend," he said. "Come in. We will have a fine dinner. And you may stay for as long as you wish."

The dog stayed with the old man and was his friend from that day on. Waldo was never hungry again. His house was never cold. And if somebody who was alone and hungry came to Waldo's house, there was always food and a warm room for the person to stay. Waldo would tell the person, "We are glad that we have so much to share with you."

The dog would wag her tail to show that she agreed.

This is the end.

snake   boat

A woman had a sick oak tree in her front yard. She called someone to cut down the tree. She told the person she called, "I live at 1234 Elm Street. Cut down the big oak tree in my front yard."

The person she called did not show up. The woman was going to call him again after she went on a walk. She was walking along when suddenly she said, "I know what happened. The tree cutter did not go to 1234 Elm Street to cut down an oak tree. The cutter went to 1234 Oak Street and cut down an elm tree. Oh dear."

1. What was the name of the street the woman lived on?

2. What was the street number?

3. Did she want the tree cutter to cut down an oak tree or an elm tree?

4. What did the cutter cut down?

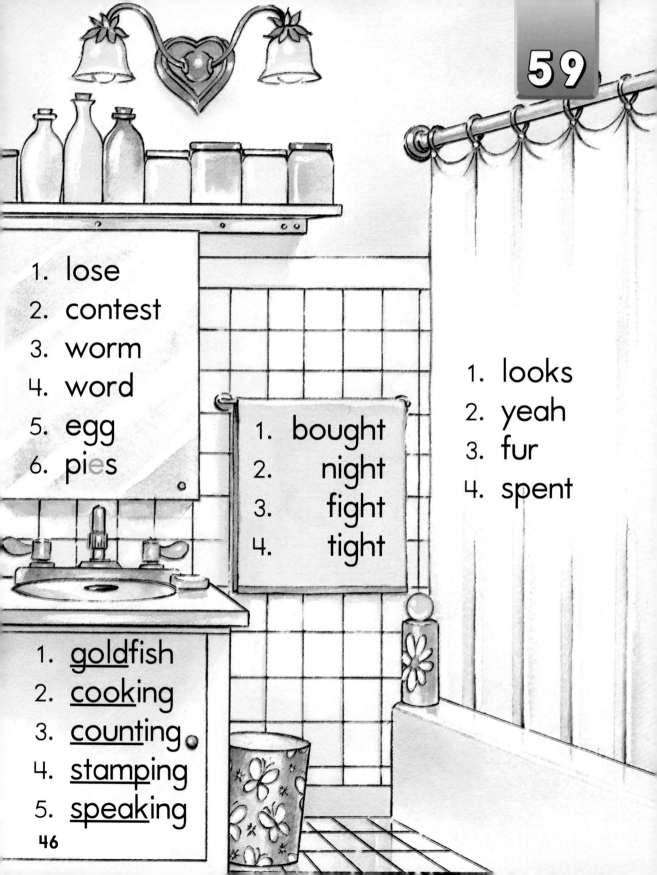

1. lose
2. contest
3. worm
4. word
5. egg
6. pies

1. bought
2. night
3. fight
4. tight

1. looks
2. yeah
3. fur
4. spent

1. goldfish
2. cooking
3. counting
4. stamping
5. speaking

The Cooking Contest
Part One

When the bragging rats did not agree, they made things bad for the other rats. Those rats had to listen to the bragging rats go on and on. One of the worst times the other rats had was when the bragging rats started bragging about how good they were at cooking. They had just spent a day yelling and bragging about how good they looked. That fight started when the rat with yellow teeth said that he looked better than any other rat in the world. The rat with the long tail said, "How can you say such lies? You look like a goldfish with fur and big yellow teeth. I am the one with the good looks."

The other rat said, "Oh yeah? Your tail looks like a big worm, and your nose looks like a lump of mud."

For the rest of the day, those rats yelled and shouted and ran around and jumped up and down. The other rats were glad when night came and the bragging rats stopped yelling.

But the next day, they started all over. This time, the rat with the long tail started it. He said, "Did you know that I am the best cook in the world?"

"You never cook anything," the other rat said.

The rat with the long tail said, "Well, everybody knows why I don't cook much. My cooking is so good that I would eat too much if I cooked, and I would get too fat."

The other rat said, "You lie like a rug. You
don't even know how to heat water on a stove."
Those rats went at it all morning—yelling,
shouting, stamping their feet, and telling big lies.

More to come.

of   front

There was a place where a farmer had a lot of cats. That place had lots of cat fur on the floor. A goat had to keep the floor clean. He would sweep the floor with a broom. At the end of the day, the farmer gave the goat something to eat. One day, the goat worked all day, sweeping fur. But at the end of the day the farmer did not give the goat any food. What did the goat do? He ate the broom.

1. What did the farmer have a lot of?

2. The place had lots of ▮▮▮▮ on the floor.

3. Who would sweep the floor?

4. When the farmer did not give the goat food, the goat ate ▮▮▮▮.

qu

ou

aw

1. places
2. laces
3. soak
4. smoke

1. eggs
2. pies
3. count
4. speak
5. bag
6. brick

1. oven
2. remember
3. crust
4. lose
5. word

1. wouldn't
2. fanning
3. baking
4. peaches

The Cooking Contest
Part Two

The bragging rats had been yelling all morning long. They were telling lies about how well they could cook. The rat with the long tail was saying, "I'm not only the best cook in the world, I'm the fastest cook in the world. My eggs are cooked before you can count to three."

Some of the other rats in the pack went to the wise old rat and said, "Isn't there something we can do to make those bragging rats shut up?"

"Yes, there is," the wise old rat said. "We will have a cooking contest. That should keep them quiet."

The wise old rat walked over to where the bragging rats were. The rat with yellow teeth was saying, "I can fix a pie so fast that it's done before you can count to one."

The other rat said, "My pies are bigger and better than any pie you can fix. And I can bake five pies before you can bake one pie."

The wise old rat said, "Stop bragging and listen to me. We will have a contest to see who makes the best pie. But you must not say a word while you make your pie. If a rat speaks, that rat will lose the contest. And the rat that loses must never brag about cooking or anything else for a year."

The wise old rat asked the bragging rats, "Do you agree?"

"Yes, yes," they said.

The rat with yellow teeth said, "I will be so quiet that nobody will know I am making the best pie in the world."

"Oh yeah?" the other rat said. "I will be so quiet that nobody will even know that I am around."

The bragging rats spent the rest of the day bragging about how quiet they would be.

More to come.

Peg and her cat lived in a place that was too small. She said, "Let's go find a place that is bigger." She saw one home she liked, but that place cost too much. She saw another place that was nice, but that place would not let her keep a cat. She looked and looked for weeks. At last, she thought of a great plan. She told her cat, "I will put two rooms onto our home, and that will make it much bigger." That's what she did.

1. Who did Peg live with?

2. Why didn't she like her home?

3. Did she find a place that she liked?

4. What did she put onto her home?

1. fa<u>ce</u>
2. spa<u>ce</u>
3. dinner
4. winner

1. taste
2. coal
3. brick
4. oar
5. crust
6. smoke

1. baking
2. fanning
3. peaches
4. bags
5. oven
6. remember

1. wear
2. skate
3. crack
4. shelf
5. blade
6. crisp

The Cooking Contest
Part Three

The next morning, the wise old rat met the rat pack in a field. He had two old ovens that burned wood. He told the bragging rats that they had to get all the things they needed to make their pies. The other rats would bring wood for the fires. Then each bragging rat would make a fire in his oven and bake a pie. The other rats would taste the pies and pick a winner.

The wise old rat said, "And remember, the rat that loses the contest must never brag for one year."

After the bragging rats left to get the things they needed to make their pies, the wise old rat led the other rats to a big pile of fire wood. That wood had been soaking in the pond. It looked dry on the outside, but it would not burn well because it was wet on the inside. The wise old rat said, "This wood will make the bragging rats stay quiet all day."

Soon the bragging rats were ready to start baking. The rat with yellow teeth had all the things he needed to make the pie crust. He also had a bag of apples. The rat with the long tail had peaches.

Those rats stared at each other, but they didn't say a word. They loaded the wet wood into their ovens and tried to start the fires, but the wood wouldn't burn. The rats tried fanning the fires and blowing on them. The only thing this fanning and blowing did was make a lot of smoke. Smoke rolled out of the ovens, but the wood did not really burn. All day long the bragging rats worked on their fires. And they were both quiet. That made the other rats very happy.

More next time.

of   boot

Two turtles wanted a swimming pool. **62**
One turtle said, "A swimming pool would
cost a lot of cash. We don't have that cash."

The other turtle said, "We could make a
swimming pool."

So they dug a big hole. Then the turtles filled
the hole with lots of water. Did they have fun
swimming in their pool? No. The water in the
hole mixed with the dirt to make a lot of mud.
The turtles did not like their pool of mud. But
their six pig friends said, "This is the best pool
there is."

1. Who wanted a swimming pool?

2. Did they have the cash they needed?

3. After they dug the hole, what did they fill it
   with?

4. Who liked the swimming pool?

1. thought
2. night
3. fight
4. high

1. mittens
2. w<u>ea</u>r
3. skat<u>e</u>
4. la<u>ce</u>s
5. blad<u>e</u>
6. coal

1. love
2. soft
3. l<u>o</u>ser
4. put
5. pull
6. push

1. crisp
2. freeze
3. crack
4. hands
5. cr<u>aw</u>l
6. brick

The Cooking Contest
Part Four

That night, the wise old rat soaked the wood again. But in the morning, the rat with the long tail came to the field with his own fire wood. He smiled at the rat with yellow teeth, but he didn't say a word. He put his dry wood on top of the wet wood that was in the oven.

In no time, his oven had a big fire in it. That fire was so hot that it dried out the wet wood, and that wood started to burn. Soon the oven was so hot that it began to turn red on the outside.

The rat with yellow teeth saw what the other rat did, so he ran off to the woods to get some dry wood. He came back with two times as much wood as the other rat had. He smiled and put the wood on top of the wet wood in his oven. Soon his oven was red hot on the outside, too.

The other rats watched. One rat whispered to the wise old rat, "If they put their pies in such hot ovens, they will burn to a crisp."

Those ovens were so hot that the rats could not stand near them without getting burned. But the rat with yellow teeth got an oar. He put his pie on the end of the oar and put it in the oven. The oven was so hot that it burned the oar. The rat with the long tail got an oar and put his pie in the oven.

Then the rats waited and waited before they tried to get their pies out of the ovens. When they did, the other rats started to laugh and howl. Those pies looked like round black bricks. One of the other rats said, "I don't want to taste those pies to see which one is best."

The only two rats that didn't laugh were the bragging rats. The one with yellow teeth said, "This contest was not fair. This is not a good oven."

The other rat said, "Yeah, look at how this bad oven turned my wonderful pie black as coal."

The wise old rat said, "You both agreed that the loser would not brag about cooking or anything else for a year. You both lose. So you both have to stop bragging for a year."

The bragging rats didn't like that, but they kept their word, and there was no bragging in the rat pack for one year.

The end.

cake   under   over

One day, a hunter was out hunting for lions. He saw two tigers and six birds. He saw three snakes and even some apes. But he didn't see any lions.

The hunter called, "Come out, nice lions." But no lions came out. He went to a cave where lions like to live. But there were no lions in it.

At the end of the day, the hunter still had not seen any lions. He was not a happy hunter. He said, "I am going home because there are no lions around here."

As he was driving away, a hundred lions came out. One of them said, "That hunter is not very good at finding lions."

1. What was the hunter hunting for?

2. He saw tigers, birds, snakes, and ▮▮▮▮▮▮.

3. Were the lions in their cave?

4. When did the lions come out?

5. Where did the hunter go?

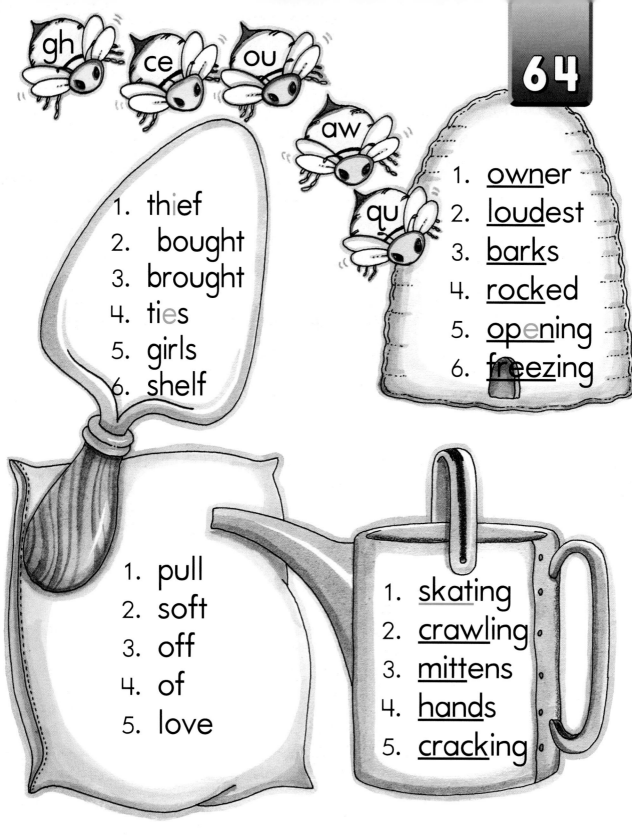

gh ce ou aw qu

1. thief
2. bought
3. brought
4. ties
5. girls
6. shelf

1. owner
2. loudest
3. barks
4. rocked
5. opening
6. freezing

1. pull
2. soft
3. off
4. of
5. love

1. skating
2. crawling
3. mittens
4. hands
5. cracking

Be Careful, Ann

We each have a blade, and we each have laces. We come out in the winter, but we don't come out as much as we would like. We are kept in a dark place that has lots of coats and mittens and other things girls put on in the winter. Do you know what we are?

Yes, we are ice skates, and we love to go skating.

We sit on a shelf and wait a long time for very cold days. We want all the water in the pond to freeze and become ice. We want to slide over that ice. Yes, yes, yes.

Now the door to the room is opening. A hand is reaching to grab us. It's Ann's hand. She pulls us off the shelf and takes us with her. This is it. Ann will put us on, and we will go skat<u>ing</u>. Yes, yes, yes.

When we reach the pond, Ann puts one foot inside each of us. Now she pulls on the laces and ties them. Now we are on the ice. Wow, we are going fast. Now we are leaving the hard ice and going on ice that is thin and soft. Oh oh, the ice is cracking. We are in the freezing water. Brrrr.

Now we are crawling out. Brrrr. Ann is taking us off. She is not having fun, and it is time for us to go home.

Next time Ann will skate where it is safe.

The end.

Ed was a little kid who loved to count things. He counted eggs. He counted trees. He counted dogs, cats, and bees. When he went on a walk, he counted the houses he walked by. He counted the cars on the street. He even counted stairs and chairs.

One day his mother said, "Oh dear. I had ten fine plates, but I can see only seven of them here. Three plates are not here."

Ed said, "Two of your plates are in a box, and one of your plates is on a shelf in the front room."

Ed's mom went to the box and found two plates. She went to the shelf in the front room and found the other plate. She said, "Ed, you are so smart."

1. What did Ed love to do?

2. What was his mother looking for?

3. Did Ed know where they were?

4. Where were two of the plates?

5. What room was the third plate in?

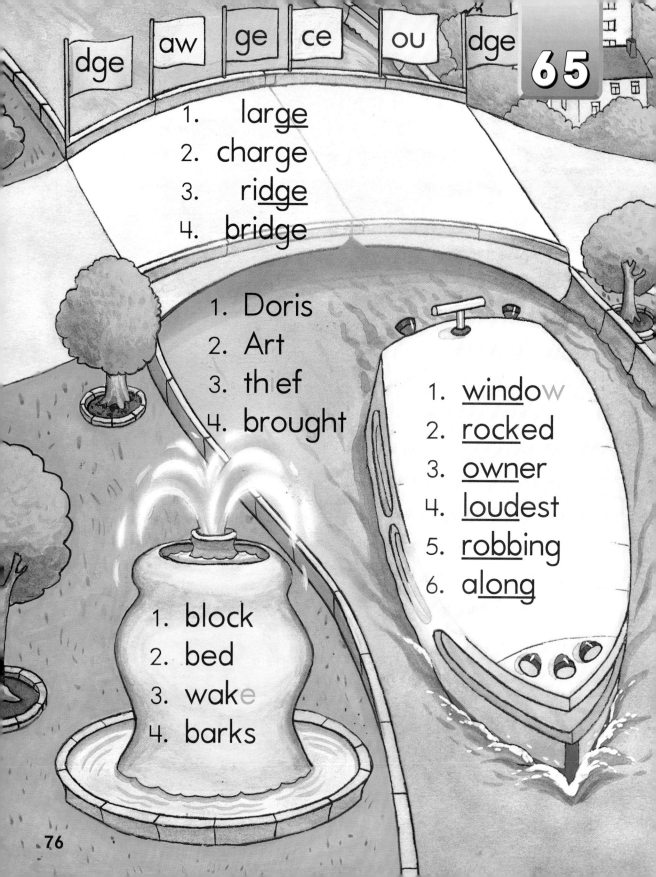

1. large
2. charge
3. ridge
4. bridge

1. Doris
2. Art
3. thief
4. brought

1. window
2. rocked
3. owner
4. loudest
5. robbing
6. along

1. block
2. bed
3. wake
4. barks

Art the Barking Cat
Part One

Doris lived in a place where she could not have a dog. But she wanted a dog because there was a thief who was doing a lot of robbing.

That thief broke into the house next to the one Doris lived in. That thief also broke into the house across the street.

Doris didn't know what to do. She thought and thought about it. At last, she went to a pet store and told the owner, "I need a watch dog, but we can't have dogs where I live. What can I do?"

The owner said, "Well, you could buy Art."

"Who is Art?" she asked.

The owner said, "Art is a watch cat."

"A watch cat?" Doris said. "That is silly. There is no such thing as a watch cat."

"Yes, there is," the owner said. "His name is Art."

Doris did not believe the owner. She said, "I have no time for bad jokes." She was getting set to leave the pet shop when the owner brought out a big brown cat with big yellow eyes. The owner said, "This is Art, the watch cat."

Doris said, "He doesn't look like he could scare a robber very much."

The owner said, "Oh yeah?" He turned to Art and said, "Speak, Art."

Art let out the loudest bark that Doris had ever heard. That bark was so loud that it rocked her and made her put her hands over her ears. "What . . . what was that?" she said.

"That was Art. He barks, and he's a very good watch cat."

Doris said, "That cat is just what I need." She bought Art and took him to her home.

More to come.

can

Jim was a mean pig. He would run around the farm every day and bite sheep, horses, and cows. The farmer said, "If you do not stop biting, I will keep you in a pen all by yourself."

Jim said, "I like to bite." He kept biting the horses, sheep, and cows. So the farmer put him in a pen all by himself.

Jim was sad. At last Clarabelle came up to Jim. She said, "To get out of this pen, you have to stop biting us. If you must bite, bite other things, like cans or pans or sticks or bricks."

Jim listened to Clarabelle and did what she said. After a while, the farmer let Jim out of the pen. He has a lot of friends on the farm now, and whenever he feels like biting, he chomps down on a big stick or an old can.

1. Who liked to bite?

2. The farmer put him in a ▨▨▨▨.

3. Before the farmer put Jim in a pen, he bit ▨▨▨▨, ▨▨▨▨, and ▨▨▨▨.

4. Now Jim bites ▨▨▨▨, ▨▨▨▨, ▨▨▨▨, and ▨▨▨▨.

ou   qu   ce   dge   aw   ge

1. block   4. wire
2. beds   5. pole
3. wakes   6. bent

1. haystack
2. window
3. tiptoe
4. loudly
5. complained

1. animal
2. finally
3. rooster
4. happening
5. along

1. edge
2. pledge
3. large
4. barge

81

Art the Barking Cat
Part Two

Doris brought Art home and fixed up a place for him to eat and sleep. On the first night she had him, a dog walked into the yard. Art let out a bark that sent leaves blowing from the trees. That bark was so loud that folks on the next block almost fell out of their beds. The poor dog in the yard got so scared that he ran like a shot, howling all the way home.

The next night, a cat came into the yard, and Art let out a bark that shook the windows. It also made that cat shake for the rest of the night.

A lot of folks complained about the barking. They told Doris, "You can't have dogs in your place." Doris tried to tell them that she didn't have a dog, but they did not believe her. They said, "If we hear any more barking, we are calling the cops."

BARK.

The next night, they called the cops. A robber and two of his pals robbed the house next to Art's house. Then they snuck into Art's yard. When they were right next to the house, Art stuck his head out of the window and let out the loudest bark you have ever heard.

That bark sent the robbers flying. Two of them landed in a small tree. Another one landed on the fence. Ouch.

Before the robbers could pick up the things they had robbed, the cops came. They were looking for a barking dog, but they f<u>ou</u>nd robbers. After the cops took the robbers to jail, they asked Doris about her dog. They didn't believe her story until she told Art to speak. Now they believe her.

Doris still has Art, and once in a while, Art barks at night and wakes up the folks all along the street. But these folks don't care, because no robbers come to that street any more.

The end.

Don bragged about how good he was at reading and playing baseball.

One day, Bonnie was walking home when she saw Don. He was sitting on the side walk with his head in his hands. Bonnie asked, "Why are you sad?"

Don said, "I tell folks I'm good at reading and playing baseball. But I can't read well. I can't play baseball well. I don't have any friends because I brag too much."

Bonnie said, "I will teach you how to read and play baseball well. And I will be your friend."

And Bonnie did those things. Soon Don was spending so much time doing things well that he didn't have time to brag.

Now Don has a lot of friends because he doesn't brag, but his best friend still is Bonnie.

1. What did Don brag about?

2. Who told Don she would be his friend?

3. What did she teach Don to do well?

4. How many friends does Don have now?

 dge ge ce aw ou

1. e<u>dge</u>
2. he<u>dge</u>
3. char<u>ge</u>
4. lar<u>ge</u>
5. loud
6. cloud

1. bent
2. wir<u>e</u>
3. pole
4. tir<u>e</u>d
5. tried
6. cried

1. <u>roo</u>ster
2. <u>hay</u>stack
3. <u>tip</u>to<u>e</u>
4. <u>windo</u>w
5. <u>happen</u>

1. cock-a-doodle-doo
2. Clarabelle
3. angry
4. pea<u>ce</u>
5. animal
6. finally

Clarabelle and the Birds
Part One

One day Clarabelle was looking at birds who were sitting on a wire. That wire went from the barn to a large pole. Clarabelle said, "I would love to sit on that wire with those birds."

Some of the other cows listened to Clarabelle talking to herself. One cow said, "Don't do it, Clarabelle. Remember what happened when you tried to swim like a duck in the duck pond?"

"Yes," another cow said. "When you jumped in the pond, all the water jumped out of the pond."

Another cow said, "And what about the time you tried to crow like a rooster? That made me laugh. You sat on the fence with the roosters. They were saying cock-a-doodle-doo. But you were saying cock-a-doodle-moo." The cows started to laugh very loudly.

"That's not funny," Clarabelle said. "And if I want to sit on that wire with those birds, you can't stop me."

So Clarabelle went into the barn and up to the window. The wire was outside that window. While she was getting ready to walk on the wire, all the farm animals gathered around.

Gorman said, "Tell me what is happening so I don't miss anything."

At last Clarabelle tiptoed out on the wire, but she was so big that the wire bent down lower and lower, until it was near the top of the haystack.

This is not the end.

next

Bob was always late. When he went on a hike with his pals, he came home late.
When he took a trip to the beach, he came home late. When he went sailing, he came home late.

One day, he was talking with a pal named Fred. Bob said, "Fred, I'm always late."

Fred said, "I think I know what you need."

"What's that?" Bob asked.

Fred said, "A watch."

Bob said, "I would like a watch, but I can't tell time."

Fred smiled and said, "Well, you are in luck. I am good at teaching how to tell time."

And so Fred showed Bob how to tell time.

1. Who was always late?

2. Did Bob have a watch?

3. Did Bob know how to tell time?

4. Who said that he would teach Bob to tell time?

5. Did Fred do that?

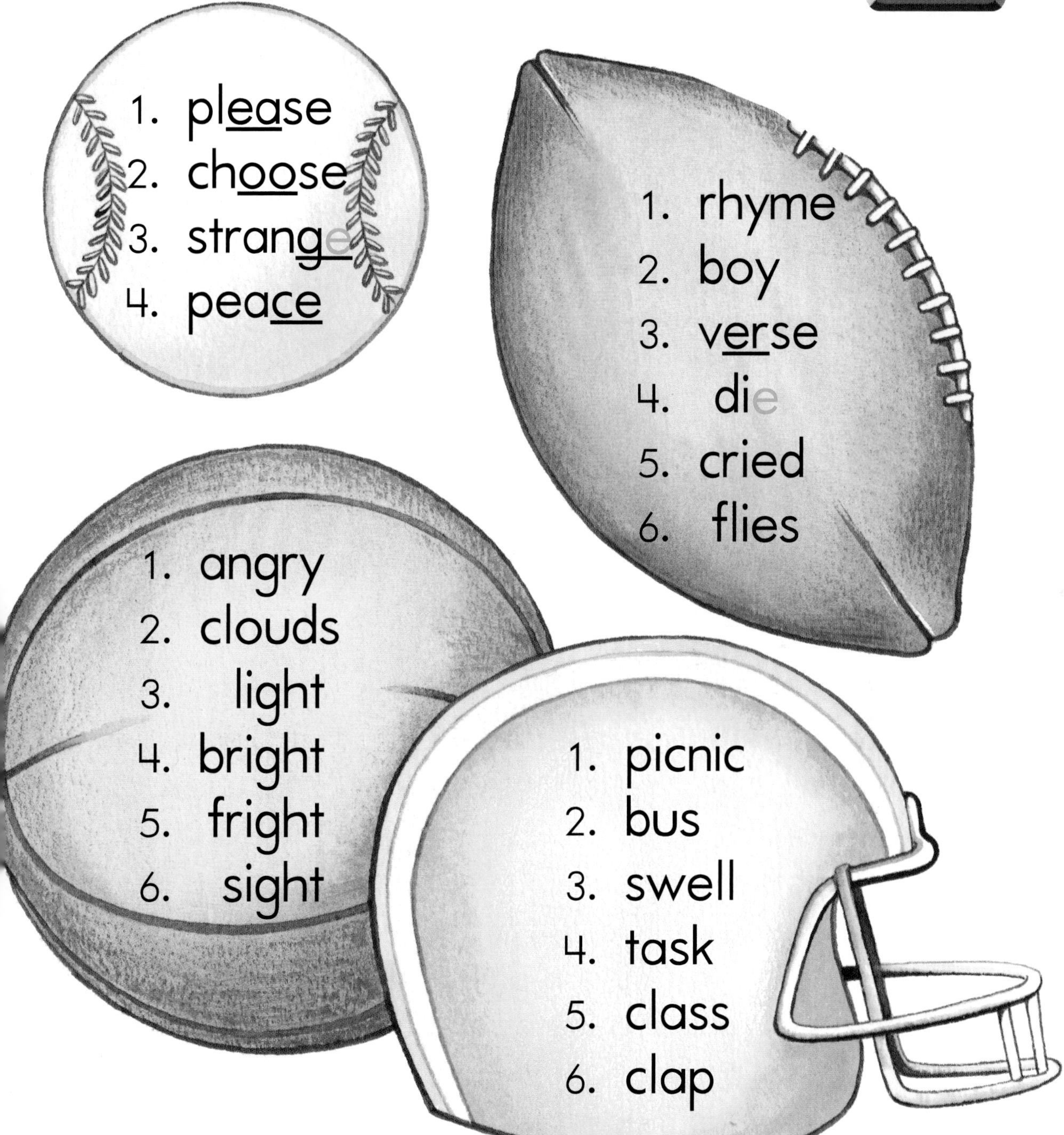

1. pl<u>ea</u>se
2. ch<u>oo</u>se
3. stran<u>ge</u>
4. pea<u>ce</u>

1. rhyme
2. boy
3. v<u>er</u>se
4. die
5. cried
6. flies

1. angry
2. clouds
3. light
4. bright
5. fright
6. sight

1. picnic
2. bus
3. swell
4. task
5. class
6. clap

Clarabelle and the Birds
Part Two

The birds were angry. They shouted at Clarabelle. One of them said, "Get off this wire. It's for birds, not big cows."

"Yes," another bird said. "We don't like sitting this close to the ground. So get off our wire."

The cows and goats and pigs and sheep were laughing and rolling around on the ground.

Clarabelle was not happy. She said to herself, "This wire is not as much fun as I thought it would be."

Clarabelle thought about going back into the window, but then she said, "It would be very hard to walk all the way up that wire."

Then Clarabelle looked down and said, "I am so close to the ground that I could jump off and land on that haystack."

As she thought about her plan, the birds kept yelling at her. "Get off our wire so we can sit in peace," they cried.

"All right," she said, and jumped off.

When she jumped off, the wire shot up into the air. It shot up so fast that it sent the birds way up into the clouds, leaving feathers all over the place.

The animals were laughing so hard that they could not stand up. The birds that had been on the wire didn't laugh, and one cow kept saying, "It's not funny."

But the rest of the farm animals thought it was very, very funny.

This is the end.

A mole was lonely. She went looking for a friend. The mole bumped into a duck and asked, "Will you be my pal?"

The duck said, "You can't swim, so I won't be your pal."

Later, the mole bumped into a hawk and asked the hawk to be her friend. The hawk told the mole that they couldn't be friends because the mole couldn't fly.

The next day, the mole bumped into another mole. They were both looking for friends. Those moles became good friends.

1. Who did the mole bump into first?

2. Who did the mole bump into next?

3. The hawk said the mole couldn't be the hawk's friend because the mole couldn't ▬▬▬▬.

4. The mole became friends with another ▬▬▬▬.

1. stage
2. picnic
3. strange
4. bus
5. boy
6. heard

1. swell
2. class
3. choose
4. vote
5. task

1. please
2. verse
3. die
4. meeting
5. fright

1. Donna
2. school
3. enter
4. parent
5. teacher
6. rhyme

I hate to wait and . . .

69

Donna
Part One

Donna was a girl who looked like a lot of other girls. But she did one thing that was strange. She talked in verse. When she stood near the bus stop, she would say things like this, "I hate to wait and get there late."

If somebody asked her what time it was, she would say something like this, "I'll tell you then. It's almost ten."

If you met her on the street and asked her how she was doing, she would say something like this, "I'm feeling well and doing swell."

When I'm done with this cake, I'll swim in the . . .

Sometimes her mom and dad would get angry with her for always talking in v<u>er</u>se. Once they were going to a picnic. Her mom said, "Please don't speak in v<u>er</u>se, Donna. Just talk the way the rest of us do."

Donna said, "You gave me a very hard task, but I'll try to do what you ask."

"Oh dear," her mom said, and shook her head.

Donna said, "Maybe I should not say even one word. I won't be bad if I can't be h<u>ea</u>rd."

But at the picnic, she spok<u>e</u>, and she spok<u>e</u> in v<u>er</u>se. Some folks thought she was funny. Some of the others thought she was very stran<u>ge</u>.

101

A little boy asked her, "How can you talk like that all the time?"

She said, "It's something I don't think about. I open my m<u>ou</u>th, and the words come out."

The boy said, "But can you make yourself talk the right way?"

She said, "I don't think that I'm able to. I speak the way I always do."

The boy shook his head and took a bite out of his hot dog. He said, "You could go on TV. You're funny."

More to come.

inside

There was a bug who had a rug. That bug took the rug with her every place she went. She took the rug to school. She took the rug to the store. She took the rug with her when she went to play. She even took the rug to bed with her. One day her mom told her, "That rug is getting dirty. I will take it and clean it for you."

But the bug would not let go of the rug. The bug said, "I will wash this rug myself." So the bug took the rug into the lake with her and washed it.

1. What did the bug have?

2. Name two places she took the rug.

3. Who told her that the rug was dirty?

4. Where did the bug wash the rug?

1. lash
2. crash
3. bright
4. sight
5. find
6. mind

1. unless
2. alive
3. stings
4. held
5. flies

1. rhymed
2. teacher
3. schools
4. entered
5. voted
6. parents

1. stage
2. die
3. fright
4. meeting

Donna
Part Two

Donna talked in verse. Donna told herself to talk the way everybody else did. And she tried. But the only time she didn't speak in verse was when she didn't know a word that rhymed.

Once she said, "My name is Donna. And I am . . . " She stopped because she didn't know a word that rhymed with Donna.

Then one day, her teacher told her that the school was going to put on a contest to see who could make up the best verse. In a little over three weeks, the children in the contest would read their verse at a large meeting.

Donna made up verse after verse, but she could only enter one verse. She didn't know which one to choose. So she asked her teacher. "Miss Brown," she said, "please help me choose. And pick the verse that will not lose."

When her teacher was done reading all of Donna's verses, she told Donna, "I really like three of them. I could read those three to the class and see what the children think."

So Miss Brown told the children, "I will read these verses to you, and you will vote for the one you like the best." Ten children liked Donna's verse about the sea. Ten children liked her verse about winter. Donna said, "We have a tie, so which will it be? The one about winter, or the one about the sea?"

The teacher said, "Let's ask another class."
And they did. That class voted for the verse about
the sea.

The time went by quickly, and soon the day of
the contest had come. All the children who
entered the contest had to stand up on a stage in
front of lots and lots of parents and children and
read their verse.

Most of the children who entered the verse
contest were pretty scared. So was Donna. Just
before she was ready to go on stage, she said to
her mom, "I don't think my verse is right. And I
think I'll die of fright."

"No, no," her mom said. "Just stand up there
and tell everybody about the sea. You'll do fine."

More to come.

Two sisters were standing on the beach near the water. The little sister said, "I hope we don't see sharks. I'm scared of sharks."

The big sister said, "Ha, ha. I am not scared of sharks. All the sharks know me. I swim with sharks. The sharks are my pals."

Just then, a big shark came over the waves.

The little sister ran away. But the big sister ran away faster. She was scared.

Later the little sister said, "Why did you run from that shark? Was that a shark you didn't know?" She knew that her sister had told a lie. Her sister did not have any shark pals.

1. Who was standing on the beach?

2. Who was scared of sharks?

3. Who said that she wasn't scared of sharks?

4. The big sister said, "The sharks are my ▮▮▮▮▮."

5. How many shark pals did the little sister think her sister had?

1. <u>ac</u>ted
2. <u>clapp</u>ing
3. <u>dropp</u>ed
4. <u>blow</u>s
5. <u>give</u>s
6. <u>trip</u>s

1. crash
2. lash
3. dive
4. alive

1. o'clock
2. lights
3. mind
4. held
5. winds

1. <u>stings</u>
2. sh<u>out</u>
3. un<u>less</u>
4. con<u>tests</u>
5. kn<u>o</u>wn

Donna
Part Three

The boy just before Donna was on the stage.
He had a very short verse. He said, "I have a
dog that is old. Her nose is always cold. I have a
cat that is white. You can see him at night. Thank
you." Everybody clapped.

Now it was Donna's turn. She walked out onto
the stage. The lights were so bright that she could
not see anybody in the crowd, but she could hear
them. She said, "My verse is called The Sea. It is
made up by me."

Donna's hands were shaking as she held up her verse. But she tried to do what her mom told her to do. Here is what Donna said.

"The winds they lash,
And the waves they crash.
Oh, how those waves roll and fall.
And there I am, alone and small.

"Beneath those clouds, so white and high,
Where rock and sun meet sea and sky,
And the sky is alive
With birds that dive,
A sharp wind blows and gives sand wings,
And so it flies, and so it stings.
The sounds and sights feed my mind
With all the things I must leave behind.
So when I go, I take with me
The birds, the clouds, the wind, and the sea."

For a little while, the crowd was quiet. Then everybody started to clap and shout. Parents were standing and clapping.

Donna won the contest. "Thank you so much," she said. She had tears in her eyes.

Later that evening, she was telling her mom and dad how she felt when she was on stage. She said, "After I started to read my verse, I felt fine, but I was very scared before I started."

Her dad said, "Do you know that you are not speaking in verse now?"

Donna thought about what she had just said. Her dad was right. Donna said, "I can't believe it. I can talk like everybody else. This is wonderful."

And from that night on, Donna never talked in verse—unless she wanted to. But she made up many verses. She won many contests, and she became very well known for her work.

The end.

clam   cup   over

Jan had to clean up all the feathers from the goose barn. There were a lot of feathers on the floor. Jan got a big broom and some bags to put the feathers in. Jan swept and swept. Soon she had all the feathers in a big pile near the door. Jan said, "Now that I am almost done, I will go outside and play." And she did. But when Jan opened the door to go out of the goose barn, the wind sent the pile of feathers all over the floor.

Later Jan went back inside to put the pile of feathers in the bag. The goose barn was a mess. "What happened to my pile?" Jan yelled.

Jan had to do her job all over again. She was not very happy, but from now on, she won't play until her jobs are done.

1. What did Jan have to clean up in the goose barn?

2. After Jan swept the feathers in a big pile, she went outside to ▮▮▮.

3. What sent the feathers all over the floor?

4. From now on, Jan won't play until her ▮▮▮ ▮▮▮ ▮▮▮.

Star:
1. <u>barges</u>
2. <u>smashes</u>
3. <u>sleek</u>est
4. <u>ramming</u>
5. <u>puff</u>ed

Moon:
1. o'clock
2. acted
3. dropped
4. friends
5. ships

Clover:
1. phew
2. motor
3. motorboat
4. bay
5. horn
6. tug

Heart:
1. <u>tubby</u>
2. <u>smoky</u>
3. <u>dumpy</u>
4. <u>slow</u>er
5. <u>stronger</u>
6. <u>pull</u>ed

A Trip to the Lake

Bob went with some friends on a field trip. Bob's mom dropped off Bob and his friends at a lake. She told them, "I'll come back and pick you up right here at three o'clock. Don't be late."

Bob's pals went looking for stones. Bob started looking at the toads that were near the lake. Then Bob walked over one hill and another hill. Soon Bob did not know where he was. He was in a field with some goats. He said to himself, "How can I find my way back to the lake?"

Follow me.

One of the goats in the field was Gorman. He heard Bob talking to himself and said, "You are not a very large moose, but I can show you how to get back to the lake."

Bob tried to tell Gorman, "I am not a moose," but Gorman did not seem to listen.

Gorman led Bob around the hills.

Go way over there.

Gorman could not see where he was going, and he didn't know where he was. But he acted as if he was leading Bob to the lake. He really led Bob to the farm house. The woman who lived there asked Bob, "Where do you want to go?"

Bob told her. Then she showed Bob which way to go.

When Bob finally got back to the lake, it was four o'clock, and his mom was waiting for him. Was she mad at him?

Bob won't be going on any field trips for a long time.

This is the end.

A skunk loved to jump rope. One day, the skunk was jumping rope on the bank of a pond. A fox came by and took the rope from the skunk. The skunk said, "Oh please, Great Fox, give me my rope back."

The fox said, "No. I want to keep this rope."

The skunk said, "Can I have the rope if I can pull it out of your hands?"

"Yes," the fox said, but the fox did not think that the skunk could do that. So the skunk pulled on the rope, and the fox pulled on the rope. Suddenly, the skunk let go, and the fox fell into the pond. While he was getting out, the skunk took the rope and ran home.

1. Who owned the jump rope?

2. Who took the rope away?

3. Did the skunk pull the rope from the fox's hands?

4. What did the skunk do to trick the fox?
   - ate the rope
   - let go of the rope
   - pulled harder on the rope

5. What did the fox fall into?

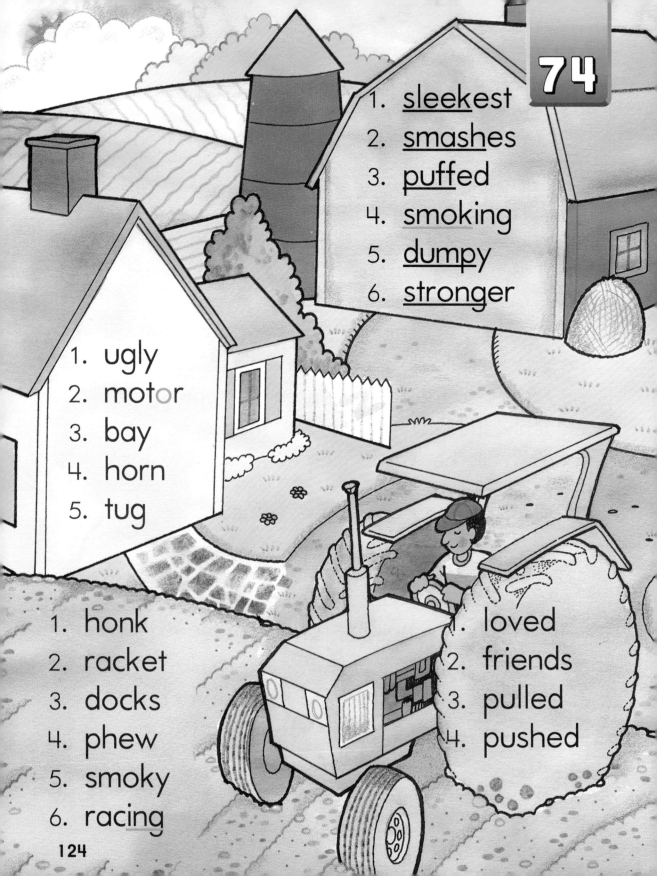

1. <u>sleek</u>est
2. <u>smash</u>es
3. <u>puff</u>ed
4. <u>smok</u>ing
5. <u>dump</u>y
6. <u>strong</u>er

1. ugly
2. motor
3. bay
4. horn
5. tug

1. honk
2. racket
3. docks
4. phew
5. smoky
6. ra<u>cing</u>

1. loved
2. friends
3. pulled
4. pushed

Tubby the Tug
Part One

Bay Town got its name because it was on a big bay. Many, many ships and boats came in and out of that bay every day. There were boats with sails and boats with motors. Some of the fastest motorboats stayed at Dock Three. Those boats loved to show off. Each boat bragged that it was the fastest and the sleekest. But all the boats knew that the boat named Red Cat was really the fastest and the sleekest.

All the other boats wanted to be friends with Red Cat. They liked to be seen near Red Cat. But those boats couldn't keep up with Red Cat when that boat was going at his fastest speed. When Red Cat was going as fast as he could go, no other boat in the bay could keep up with him. Red Cat would dart around the barges and the slower ships.

Sometimes Red Cat would get very close to them, and they would blow their horns. But Red Cat didn't mind if the other boats got mad. What could they do about it?

One of the boats at Dock Three was as slow as Red Cat was fast. That boat was as dumpy as Red Cat was sleek. That boat was a smoky old tug named Tubby. All the other boats said "phew" when Tubby puffed in and out of the bay to do her work.

Most of the other boats were fun boats, but Tubby was a work boat. Tubby was ten times slower than Red Cat, but she was ten times stronger than Red Cat. Tubby's job was to pull and push the biggest ships in the bay.

Tubby was almost as strong as those large ships. And Tubby needed to be strong to keep the large ships from running into things. Tubby had to steer them away from the places where the bay was not deep. Tubby had to keep them from ramming into the docks. If a large ship runs into the docks, it keeps right on going and smashes everything before it finally stops.

This is not the end.

Peggy wanted to paint her porch pink. So she got three pails of pink paint and some brushes. Peggy asked two of her pals to come and help her paint.

Each girl had a brush and a can of pink paint. Peggy started with the front of the house, and her two pals painted the floor.

When they were done, Peggy was standing in the only part of the porch that wasn't pink. "Help, help," Peggy said. "I'm stuck on the porch."

Peggy's pals laughed. "You will have to stay there until the porch is dry."

But Peggy did not want to stay. She painted the part that wasn't pink. Then she walked across the wet paint. Now the porch is pink, and Peggy's feet are pink.

1. What did Peggy want to paint?

2. Peggy wanted to paint it ▮▮▮▮.

3. Peggy said, "I'm ▮▮▮▮ on the porch."

4. How did Peggy get across the wet paint?

5. Now what things are pink?

1. barge
2. charge

3. boy
4. toy

1. ugly
2. awake
3. trap
4. bother
5. blast

1. <u>honked</u>
2. <u>pushing</u>
3. <u>puffing</u>
4. <u>blocks</u>
5. <u>blown</u>
6. <u>against</u>

1. head   2. heavy   3. slept
    4. rest   5. smell

Tubby the Tug
Part Two

It was six o'clock in the morning, and Tubby was starting her motor and puffing out smoke. The other boats at the dock woke up and started complaining. "We're trying to rest," they said. "What are you making all that racket for—and all that smoke? Phew."

"I can't help it," Tubby said. "I have to go to work."

"Well, go," Red Cat said. "And don't come back. I can't even nap when you're around. You smell bad."

So Tubby honked her horn three times and went off to push and pull the big ships in and out of the bay. The other boats got mad when Tubby honked her horn, but Tubby kept telling them, "I have to honk my horn three times when I start work, and three times when I stop."

Around noon, the other boats at Dock Three
came out to play. They darted around the bay and
made waves. They laughed as they chased each
other.

Tubby watched them, but only once in a while.
The rest of the time, she had to watch what she
was doing and where she was pushing ships and
barges.

Once in a while, two or three of the fast boats would speed past Tubby and say something like, "Tubby, do you want to ra<u>ce</u>?"

That would make Tubby feel bad. Tubby knew that a ra<u>ce</u> with those boats would not be much of a contest. Tubby would only go a hundred feet in the time the other boats would go a mile.

So Tubby worked, and the others played. And at the end of the day, when Tubby had put the last ship in place, she would honk her horn three times and go back to Dock Three. Tubby tried to keep her motor quiet so she wouldn't make too much smoke, but the other boats complained. "This is a no smok<u>ing</u> dock," one of them yelled. "Get that smok<u>ing</u> tug out of here."

One of the very sleek boats said to the boat next to it, "There goes one ugly boat. Phew."

Tubby went to the end of the dock and tried to rest. It wouldn't be long before Tubby had to go to work again.

More to come.

Dave and Bob were going to a party that their friend Jan was having. Bob and Dave were picking things to give Jan.

Dave said to Bob, "Jan will like what I give her more than she will like what you give her."

Bob said, "I do not care if Jan likes what you give her better. I just hope she likes all of her presents."

The day of the party, Jan and Dave and five of their friends were at the party. They were waiting for Bob to come before they cut the cake. Bob was late.

At last Bob came, and they had cake. After everyone was done eating the cake, Jan opened the things her friends brought her. Did she like what Dave brought her more? No. Dave and Bob gave her the same thing.

75

1. Whose party were Bob and Dave going to?

2. Who wanted Jan to like all of her presents?

3. What did they wait to do until Bob got there?

4. Why didn't Jan like Dave's present more than Bob's present?

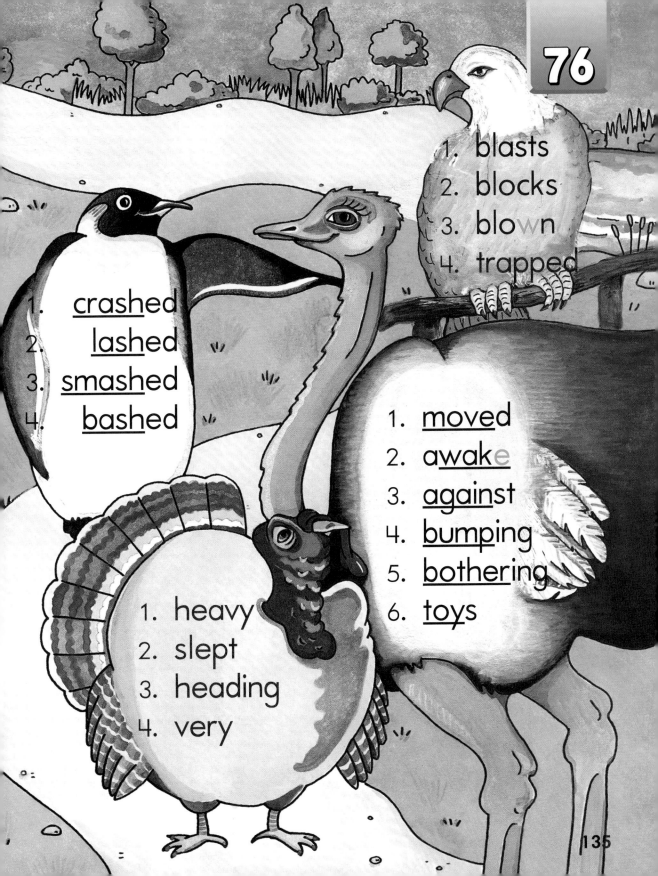

1. blasts
2. blocks
3. blown
4. trapped

1. <u>crashed</u>
2. <u>lashed</u>
3. <u>smashed</u>
4. <u>bashed</u>

1. <u>moved</u>
2. <u>awake</u>
3. <u>against</u>
4. <u>bumping</u>
5. <u>bothering</u>
6. <u>toys</u>

1. heavy
2. slept
3. heading
4. very

Tubby the Tug
Part Three

That night, when Tubby and the other boats at Dock Three were sleeping, a very bad storm raced into the bay. The winds lashed out and rolled the water into large waves. Soon those waves were crashing against the docks. They were also crashing against the ships and barges. One barge that was longer than three blocks was blown out of place.

The wind and waves were pushing that barge right at Dock Three. Most of the speed boats were awake now, but the crashing waves had them trapped next to the dock. One of them saw the barge coming closer and closer to the dock. "Help, help," that boat called out. "Who can help me get free?"

The other boats were tugging at their ropes and shouting at each other. "Stop bumping into me," Red Cat shouted to the boat next to him.

"I can't help it," that boat said. "The waves are pushing me into you."

While all this was going on, Tubby was sleeping. All the wind and the waves were not bothering that old tug boat. She rocked a little, but she was ten times as heavy as the other boats and didn't mind wind and waves. So she slept.

The barge was very close to the dock now. It was so big that it made the dock look very small and made those boats look like little toys.

Then the barge made three loud horn blasts. Honk, honk, honk. It was trying to let everybody know that it was heading for the dock.

Those blasts woke Tubby. When Tubby heard them, she thought it was time to go to work. So Tubby quickly started her motor and let out three horn blasts. Red Cat and the others heard Tubby's blasts and saw the smoke. "Help us, Tubby. We're going to be smashed. Help us."

"Wow," Tubby said when she saw how close the barge was. "I don't know if I can stop that barge in time."

"Oh, please try. Please," the other boats cried.

More next time.

Last summer, Ted had a job picking apples. Ted picked apples all day long. He picked red apples, and he picked green apples. Ted tried not to pick apples that had holes in them or apples that had brown spots.

Every day after work, Ted got to take home all the apples he wanted. He ate some of the apples. With other apples, he made pies. He put the rest of them in jars and cans. Ted loved picking apples and eating them.

1. What was Ted's job?

2. Did Ted like his job?

3. Were all of the apples good apples?

4. What did Ted get to take home with him?

aw gh ge ce ch qu ou

1. b**oi**l
2. j**oi**n
3. p**oi**nt
4. v**oi**ce

1. act
2. sneak
3. m**ou**se
4. gray
5. tease
6. co**ur**se

1. nice
2. mice
3. p**ou**nce

1. mountain
2. valley
3. smash
4. moved
5. moving
6. bright

Tubby the Tug
Part Four

A large barge was coming right at Dock Three. If something didn't stop that barge very soon, the barge would smash Red Cat and the other boats. "Help," Red Cat cried. "Please save us."

Tubby was trying to do that. The tug puffed out smoke and went as fast as she could. Honk, honk, honk. But the barge kept moving closer and closer to Dock Three.

Tubby went between the barge and the dock. Then Tubby pushed against the side of the barge as hard as she could. But the barge didn't stop. It was now very close to the motorboats.

Tubby saved us.

Tubby kept pushing and puffing and puffing and pushing. And the barge started moving slower and slower. Then it stopped. Then it moved slowly back. Tubby was pushing that barge against the waves and the wind. The other boats saw what Tubby was doing.

"Tubby saved us," Red Cat shouted.

The boats cheered and shouted, but Tubby still had a lot of work to do. After a long time, Tubby pushed that barge way out in the bay where it should be.

Tubby's motor worked so hard that parts of it started to burn up. When the barge was finally in place, Tubby stopped out there in the bay. Honk, honk, honk. The other boats knew that Tubby's motor had blown up.

"I'll save Tubby," Red Cat said as he got free from the dock. Red Cat raced out into the bay, grabbed Tubby's tow rope, and pulled the little tug back to the dock. Red Cat never worked so hard before, but he was glad to do it.

Today, Tubby's motor is fixed. And Tubby has a coat of bright red paint, just like Red Cat. And Tubby has a place right next to Red Cat at Dock Three. Tubby still honks and puffs smoke and goes to work every morning. But the other boats don't complain. And no boats make fun of Tubby as they speed by. They wave and say the things that pals say when they see each other. "How are you doing?" They are pr**ou**d to have Tubby as their friend.

The end.

There was a barge that didn't like tug boats. The barge said, "Those tugs are always bumping into my side and trying to push me around."

One day, the barge was going into a bay when a tug boat came near. The barge said, "I don't need your help. I can find a good place in the bay by myself."

Just then a big wind pushed the barge all the way to the shore. "Help, help," the barge called. "Who can move me away from the shore?"

The tug said, "I could do it. But you'll have to be nice to me." The barge agreed. So the tug pulled the barge away from the shore. Now the tug and the barge are good friends.

1. Who did not like tugs?

2. Who said, "I don't need your help"?

3. A wind came up when the barge was heading into a ▇▇▇▇▇.

4. That wind pushed the barge all the way to the ▇▇▇▇▇.

5. Where did the tug pull the barge?

L

1. <u>sound</u>ed
2. <u>follow</u>ing
3. <u>mountains</u>
4. <u>valley</u>s
5. <u>any</u>where
6. <u>pain</u>ting

A

1. phone
2. of course
3. moving
4. lovely
5. robot

M

1. p<u>oi</u>nt
2. v<u>oi</u>ce
3. b<u>oi</u>l

S

1. sneak
2. speak
3. ray
4. gray
5. nice
6. mice

P

1. sli<u>c</u>es
2. people
3. perfect
4. toaster

I can't tell if we are moving.

Rolla Slows Down

When we left Rolla, she was very happy. She was number 1. She went up and down at the right speed. The music sounded fine. The children were happy, and their mothers were happy.

Things went on like this for weeks. But then one day, something happened. Rolla said to herself, "I am number 1, but I am right behind number 8." Rolla thought that she should be far away from number 8. Then it would look as if she was the leader and the other horses were following her.

Rolla said, "I will get far from horse 8." To do that, Rolla slowed down. She went slower, and slower, and slower. But of course her plan didn't work. When she went slower, all the other horses went slower. The music slowed down and sounded awful. The mothers were unhappy. One of them said, "This merry-go-round is so slow, you can't tell if it's going or if it has stopped."

The other horses were not happy with Rolla. Horse 2 kept shouting at Rolla, "Come on, Rolla. Let's get this merry-go-round moving." But Rolla tried as hard as she could to slow down.

At the end of the day, horse 8 was still there, right in front of her.

That evening, horse number 3 asked, "What are you trying to do?"

When Rolla told them, some of the horses started to laugh. Then horse number 5 said, "Rolla, would you be happy if you could not see horse 8?"

"Yes," Rolla said. "If I could not see that horse, I would not feel like I was following it. I would feel like the leader."

So the other horses got together and did a lot
of talking. When they were done, they smiled and
told Rolla they would fix things up.

The next day when Rolla woke up, she looked in
front of her and saw mountains and valleys. They
were lovely. She couldn't see another horse
anywhere in front of her. After a while, she found
out that the other horses had made a painting and
put it between her and horse 8. But Rolla didn't
care. She felt wonderful leading the other horses
into the mountains.

So everything is fine now. The horses are happy.
The music sounds good. And the mothers and
children like the merry-go-round even more than
before.

The end.

A boy named Ted was always thinking. He would think in the morning. He would think when he ate lunch. He would think in school and at home. One day, his sister said to him, "Why do you spend so much time thinking?"

Ted said, "I don't know. Let me think about that."

So Ted thought about why he thought. This went on for five days.

Then he told his sister, "I don't know why I think so much. But I think I'm tired of thinking. Let's do something else."

So they went bike riding.

1. Who always thought?

2. He thought at home and in ▮▮▮▮.

3. Who asked him why he thought so much?

4. Did Ted know why he thought so much?

5. What did Ted and his sister do after Ted got tired of thinking?

oi   ea   ou   ge   gh   ce

1. mice
2. slice
3. voice
4. choice

1. <u>folding</u>
2. <u>corner</u>
3. <u>recall</u>
4. <u>dishes</u>
5. <u>toaster</u>

1. Molly
2. Bleep
3. perfect
4. robot
5. hello
6. hung

1. elm
2. mess
3. people
4. phone
5. tigers

Molly and Bleep
Part One

Molly was a very smart woman. She made a lot of things that were very smart. She made toasters and folding chairs and even racing boats. But none of the things she made were perfect. Her toaster toasted six slices at the same time, but three of them were too dark. Her folding chairs folded when someone was sitting in them. One of Molly's pals was stuck in a folding chair for a long time before Molly found her.

Molly's racing boats were very fast and very strong. When they were going very fast, they were wonderful. But when they slowed down, they would get so low in the water that a little wave could sink them.

The best thing that Molly made was a robot named Bleep. She worked on Bleep every day in her shop. It took her six years to make that robot. When she was done, Bleep was almost perfect.

Bleep could get the mail, go to the store, and ride a bike. He could also do many things you told him to do. He could even speak. His voice sounded just like Molly's. But when Bleep spoke, he did two things that Molly did not do. Most of the time, Bleep started out by saying, "Bleep." And when someone told Bleep to do something, he would say, "Okay, baby."

No, Bleep.

Bleep could also talk on the phone and tell Molly what people said. If the phone rang while Molly was working on her folding chair or her racing boat, Bleep would talk on the phone. Later he would tell Molly what the person said. But Bleep would sometimes tell big lies. One time, Bleep talked on the phone and then said to Molly, "Bleep. Your mother just called. She found four tigers in the yard."

More to come.

Two ants named Tam and Sid lived far away from each other. They were best friends. But it took a lot of work to see each other, because they lived so far apart. One day, Tam would have to walk all the way to Sid's house and back. The next day, Sid would have to walk all the way to Tam's house and back. Those are very long walks for ants.

One day, Sid came up with a plan. Sid said, "We could both walk toward each other's house and meet somewhere in between. That way, we wouldn't have to walk as far."

So the ants tried that. But it didn't work. Sid didn't see Tam, and Tam didn't see Sid. Sid ended up at Tam's house, and Tam ended up at Sid's house.

1. Why did it take a lot of work for Tam and Sid to be best friends?

2. Where did Sid plan to meet Tam?

3. Did the plan work?

4. Where did Tam end up?

5. Where did Sid end up?

aw oi ge ou ce

1. sled
2. hello
3. corner
4. elm
5. recall
6. hung

1. Mrs. Anderson
2. heard
3. dishes
4. book
5. wonder
6. fence

1. sign
2. great
3. lied
4. zone
5. junk
6. sport

1. tease
2. please
3. mouse
4. house

Molly and Bleep
Part Two

Bleep was a robot that was almost perfect. But he did one thing that was not perfect. Sometimes he told big lies. And sometimes those lies made a big mess. The biggest mess that Bleep made happened when Mrs. Anderson called. She was a friend of Molly's. She had never met Bleep or heard his voice. Molly was in her shop working on a racing sled. Bleep was washing the dishes. When the phone rang, Bleep picked it up and said, "Bleep. Hello."

Mrs. Anderson did not know that she was talking to Bleep. She thought she was talking to Molly. So she said, "You know that we are to meet for lunch today."

Bleep said, "Bleep. Yes."

Mrs. Anderson said, "Well, it is your turn to pick a place where we will eat. Where do you want to go?"

Bleep said, "Bleep. I like the place on the corner of First and Elm."

Mrs. Anderson said, "First and Elm? I don't recall anything on that corner."

Bleep said, "Bleep. It is a fine place. You will like it a lot."

Mrs. Anderson said, "Well then, I will see you on the corner of First and Elm around noon." Then she said, "Could you also bring that book you wanted me to read?"

Bleep said, "Okay, baby."

Bleep hung up the phone and went back to washing the dishes. Pretty soon, Molly came in from her shop. She asked, "Did anyone call for me?"

Bleep said, "Bleep. Yes. Mrs. Anderson called about lunch today."

"Good," Molly said. "Where does she want to eat?"

Bleep said, "Bleep. The corner of First and Elm."

Molly said, "First and Elm? I don't recall a place to eat on that corner."

Bleep said, "Bleep. Mrs. Anderson said that it is a wonderful place to eat. Yum, yum."

Molly said, "That sounds good. Did she say anything else?"

Bleep said, "Bleep. Mrs. Anderson says that you should bring one of your folding chairs."

Molly shook her head. "I wonder why she wants a chair."

More next time.

Sandy was not very good at math. When she wanted to make a six, she would make a nine. When she wanted to make a two, she would make a five. Sandy also had a hard time with math problems. If the problem said to add six and two, Sandy could not put down the right numbers. She would add nine and five.

Sandy was sad. She asked her teacher to help her with her math. So her teacher worked with Sandy. Now Sandy is very good in math. She no longer mixes up six and nine, or two and five. Before long, Sandy could work any math problem that her teacher gave. She could even add three numbers at a time.

1. What was Sandy poor at?

2. Which number did Sandy write for six?

3. Which number did Sandy write for two?

4. How did Sandy get better at math?

5. Who helped her?

ge ch sh th ce aw

1. maker
2. lady
3. sign
4. zone
5. great
6. lied

1. family
2. whisper
3. matter
4. parked
5. p<u>ou</u>nce
6. choice

1. rule
2. sorry
3. junk
4. sport
5. rods
6. act

Why does she want a folding chair?

Molly and Bleep
Part Three

Bleep talked on the phone and told Mrs. Anderson one big lie. Then Bleep talked to Molly and told her two big lies.

Molly did not know why Mrs. Anderson wanted a folding chair, but Molly told Bleep to load the chair into her van. Molly loved her van. It was red, and it was big. So it had lots of room for the things that Molly needed when she made something like a racing sled or a cake maker.

Molly drove her red van to the corner of First and Elm. She didn't see a place to eat. She didn't see Mrs. Anderson's car. The only thing she saw was a big junk yard. So she parked her car by the fence in front of the junk yard. There was a sign on the fence. That sign said "Drop Off Zone." Molly didn't know what a drop off zone was.

She got out of her car and walked along Elm Street. She was looking for Mrs. Anderson or the place where they would eat. But all she saw was a great junk yard. Molly kept walking and looking for Mrs. Anderson's car. That car was very easy to see. It was a bright red car, just like Molly's van. But Mrs. Anderson's car was a small sport car, not a big van.

While Molly was looking for Mrs. Anderson, Mrs. Anderson drove up to the corner of First and Elm. She saw Molly's van in the drop off zone. So she parked next to the van. Then she got out and started to look for Molly. She said to herself, "It is hard to believe that there is a good place to eat on this street." But she walked down Elm Street. At last she saw Molly.

She called to Molly and said, "Where is there a place to eat around here?"

Molly said, "I don't know. Bleep said you wanted to come here."

"Not so," Mrs. Anderson said. "When we talked on the phone, you told me that you wanted to come here."

Molly said, "Oh dear. You didn't talk to me on the phone. You talked to Bleep. I think Bleep lied to both of us."

This is not the end.

Jane and her pals went to hear some singers who were really good. They all got into Jane's van and went down town. Lots of people were there to listen to the singers. When Jane and her pals sat down, it was just about time for the singing to start.

The singers came out and sang two songs. When they started the third song, one of them began to sneeze. Then the rest of them sneezed. They sneezed until the end of the song. Jane and her pals liked the sneezing song a lot. Then they started to sneeze, too. Before long, everybody was sneezing.

1. Who did Jane go with?

2. Who did they hear?

3. How many songs did they sing without sneezing?

4. Did Jane and her pals like the sneezing song?

5. What did everyone do after that song?

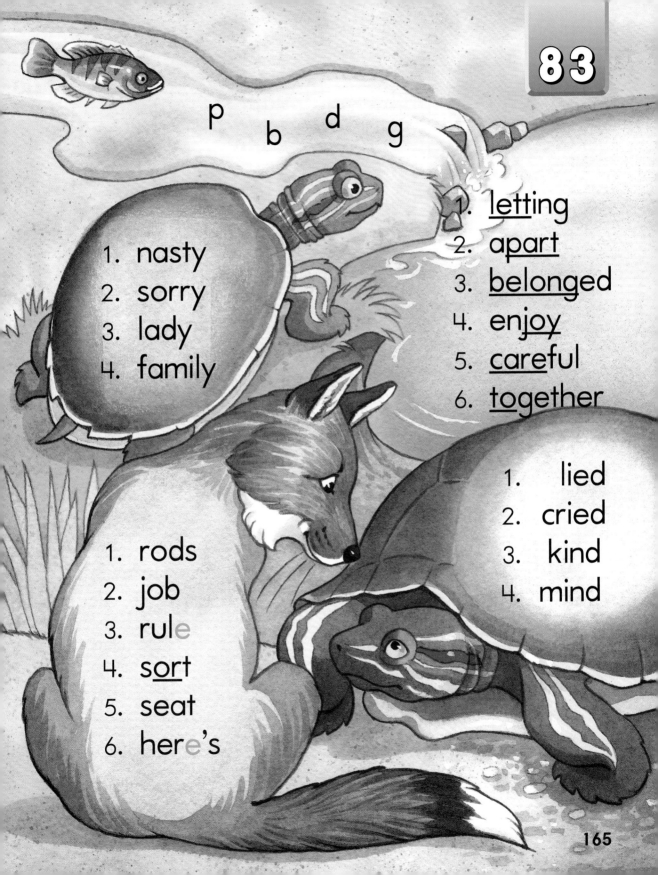

83

p b d g

1. nasty
2. sorry
3. lady
4. family

1. letting
2. apart
3. belonged
4. enjoy
5. careful
6. together

1. lied
2. cried
3. kind
4. mind

1. rods
2. job
3. rule
4. sort
5. seat
6. here's

165

Molly and Bleep
Part Four

Molly and Mrs. Anderson found out that Bleep had lied to both of them.

They laughed about it. Molly said, "I'll have to be careful about letting Bleep talk on the phone." Then Molly and Mrs. Anderson started to walk back to the corner of First and Elm.

When they got back to the drop off zone, Molly said, "Where is my van?"

Mrs. Anderson said, "Where is my car?"

Speech bubble: "Sorry. We just followed the rule."

Molly and Mrs. Anderson saw a worker, so they called to him and asked about the cars.

He said, "Here's the rule about the drop off zone. If cars are left in the drop off zone, we take them apart. Your cars were in the drop off zone. So your cars are no longer cars."

"No longer cars?" Mrs. Anderson shouted. "You can't take my car apart."

The worker said, "Sorry. We just followed the rule about cars in the drop off zone."

Then the worker led Molly and Mrs. Anderson inside the junk yard. He took them to a large pile of car parts. He said, "Well, this pile is what's left of your cars."

That door goes to the van.

Mrs. Anderson said, "This is awful." She turned to the worker and said, "You took the cars apart, so now you can put them back together, just the way they were."

"Sorry, lady," the worker said. "We just take things apart. We don't know how to put them back together."

Mrs. Anderson started to cry.

Molly said, "I am pretty good at making things. If we can get some of the workers to help us, we can get these cars back together before it is time for dinner."

Four workers helped. Mrs. Anderson helped, too. Molly was in charge. She told the others where to put the rods and the doors and the other parts.

More to come.

Brett's family had a house on a lake. Last year, Brett's parents let his friend Mike stay with him for the week. The boys swam and went boating, hiking, and fishing. Soon it was time for Mike to go home. But Mike said, "I want to stay out here for the rest of the summer."

So Mike went to Brett's parents and said, "Can I stay out here if I do all the jobs around the house?"

They said yes. So Mike worked hard every morning to get his jobs done. Then he spent the rest of each day having fun with Brett. Everybody was happy.

1. Where was the house?

2. Who did Brett have come stay with him?

3. At first, how long was Mike going to stay?

4. How long did he stay?

5. Who had to do jobs around the house?

6. Was Mike happy?

1. s<u>or</u>t
2. cheeks
3. afraid
4. job
5. tease
6. ha<u>ll</u>

1. new
2. family
3. putting
4. tickle
5. giggle
6. ugly

1. en<u>joy</u>
2. be<u>long</u>ed
3. to<u>night</u>
4. <u>tog</u>ether
5. <u>party</u>

Molly and Bleep
Part Five

Molly, Mrs. Anderson, and four workers from the junk yard put the cars back together. By dinner time, there were two red cars inside the junk yard, but those two cars were not the same as the cars that drove up to the junk yard. There was no longer a van and a little sport car. There were two things that were part van and part sport car.

One of them looked like a van in front and a sport car in back. The other looked like a sport car in front and a van in back. That one had two seats and Molly's folding chair in it. Mrs. Anderson looked at the cars and started to cry again.

Molly said, "Well, I did the best I could, but all the parts were red. So I didn't always know which part belonged to which car." The workers were laughing pretty hard. One of them said, "Those are two ugly cars."

Mrs. Anderson cried, "Yes, very ugly."

Molly said, "I don't know. I think those cars look sort of pretty."

The workers laughed harder than before.

Molly told Mrs. Anderson, "Well, pick one of these things, and I'll take the other."

So Mrs. Anderson drove home in one of the red things. At home she cried and cried. Molly drove home in the other red thing. Then she looked at it a long time and said to herself, "Those workers are right. This thing is ugly."

When Molly went inside, Bleep said, "Bleep. Did you enjoy lunch?"

Molly said, "No, I didn't." For a moment, she thought about taking Bleep back to the junk yard and leaving him in the drop off zone. But then she said, "From now on, you may not talk on the phone."

Bleep said, "Okay, baby."

The next day, three workers, Molly, and Bleep put the cars back together the right way. The workers were from a car shop. One of them was very good at putting cars together. He told Molly and the others where the parts went. When the job was done, Mrs. Anderson was very happy, and so was Molly.

The end.

A snail named Gail wanted to swim. She ran and jumped into a stream. Did she swim? No. She just sank to the bottom. She didn't have any arms or legs to swim with, so she had to creep along the bottom of the stream until she could get out of the water. That was no fun.

The next day, Gail tried to swim again. She went to another part of the stream and jumped in. Did she swim? No. She sank to the bottom of the stream. Gail just could not swim.

On the third day, Gail asked a turtle, "Could I sit on your back while you go swimming?"

The turtle said, "Yes." So Gail got on the turtle's back, and they went swimming. Gail said, "I knew I could swim if I just kept trying."

1. What did Gail want to do?

2. On the first day, what happened when Gail tried to swim?

3. What did she creep along to get out of the water?

4. Did she try to swim the next day?

5. Who helped Gail swim?

oi ou aw dge ce ai

1. ew
2. new
3. chew
4. flew

1. Patty
2. Arnold
3. act
4. matter
5. room
6. boom

1. <u>a</u>fraid
2. <u>to</u>night
3. <u>g</u>i<u>gg</u>le
4. <u>tick</u>le
5. <u>n</u>as<u>t</u>y

1. whisp<u>er</u>
2. l<u>ou</u>dly
3. sn<u>ea</u>king
4. gr<u>ay</u>
5. poun<u>ce</u>
6. <u>ch</u>eeks

176

Patty and the Cats
Part One

There once was a very large mouse named Patty. She lived with her mom and dad and her six brothers and nine sisters.

All the other mice in her family were nice and quiet. Each one spoke in a tiny voice. When the house was dark at night, they snuck around without making a sound.

Patty did not act like the others in her family. She could not speak in a tiny voice. Even when she tried to speak in a whisper, her voice was loud.

When she went with the others at night, she spoke so loudly that she scared them. They were scared because a large gray cat named Arnold lived in the house. If Arnold found the mice while they were sneaking around looking for food, he would p<u>ou</u>nce on them. When Patty said something at night, her brothers and sisters would say, "Shshshsh." But no matter how hard she tried to talk quietly, her voice boomed out.

Please . . .

Patty's brothers gave her the name "Big Mouse the Big Mouth." She didn't like that name, but her voice was too loud. And if her brothers teased her too much, she could just say, "Please stop teasing me," and her voice would blow them over.

More next time.

Seth was a rac<u>oo</u>n who lived with his mother and father. His mother and father asked Seth to leave because he made messes and did not clean up. Seth walked around the forest looking for another place to live.

Seth found a mole who was living under the ground near a tree. Seth told the mole why he had to leave home. The mole told Seth, "I am good at cleaning up, but I don't know how to cook."

Seth said, "I am a good cook." So Seth showed the mole how to cook, and the mole showed Seth how to clean up. Seth and the mole are both happy now.

1. Seth's mother and father asked him to ▬▬▬▬.
   - leave home
   - cook food
   - cut down a tree

2. Who did Seth find living near a tree?

3. Who could cook well?

4. Who could clean up well?

5. Are Seth and the mole happy now?

ew oi aw ar dge

1. visiting
2. party
3. shadows
4. living

1. cheeks
2. smells
3. halls
4. friends

1. house
2. mouse
3. louder
4. shouting

1. chew
2. blew
3. news

1. toward
2. warn
3. through
4. kitchen
5. heard

Patty and the Cats
Part Two

Patty could not speak in a soft voice. But if you think her talking voice was loud, you should have heard her shouting voice. It was many times louder. That shouting voice was so loud that it shook the house. It made anybody near Patty have ringing ears.

One time, she was playing with some of her brothers and sisters. They started to tickle her, and she started to giggle. Then she started to laugh and shout. She shouted so loudly that she sent two of her sisters sailing into the air. Three of her brothers had such ringing in their ears that they did not hear well for six days.

That night, Patty was getting ready to go out with her family when her mom gave her some very bad news. "Patty," her mom said. "You can't go out with us tonight. It is just not safe."

"Oh, please let me go," Patty said. "I'll be quiet. I won't say a word."

"I'm sorry," her mom said. "You have to stay inside our home."

Patty was very sad, but she did what her mom said. She watched the others go out. She felt big tears form in her eyes and run down her cheeks.

Patty's mom and dad were afraid because there were new smells in the house. Those were the smells of new cats. The mice didn't know it, but Arnold had four friends that were visiting him. They were large, nasty cats who loved to chase mice and pounce on them.

This is not the end.

Jean and her brother did not know how to ride bikes. Jean's brother said, "I don't want to try to ride a bike." And he started to cry.

Jean said, "I do not know how to ride, but I will give it a good try." And she did.

Both Jean and her brother did not know how to read. Jean's brother cried, but Jean tried.

After a while, Jean could read and ride bikes. Jean's brother could not read or ride. Jean's brother was good at doing only one thing. He was good at crying.

1. Who tried to read?

2. Who didn't try?

3. At the end of the story, what could Jean do?
   - sit and cry
   - read and ride bikes
   - sing and play

4. Jean's brother was better than Jean at ▮▮▮▮.

oi ew oy aw ou

1. expl<u>ai</u>n
2. p<u>aw</u>
3. p<u>ar</u>ty
4. <u>edge</u>
5. p<u>ai</u>nting

1. <u>ce</u>iling
2. knocked
3. warn
4. kitchen
5. joy

1. flick
2. cheese
3. brave
4. shadow

1. toward
2. living
3. through
4. save

1. <u>back</u>ward
2. <u>be</u>hind
3. <u>a</u>long
4. <u>pouncing</u>

Patty and the Cats
Part Three

Arnold had asked four friends to come over to his place. He told them that his house had lots of mice and that the cats would have a great pouncing party.

Patty was inside her home, looking out the mouse hole at her family. She could see her dad lead the way toward the kitchen. The others followed slowly along the edge of the rug in the living room. Then they snuck down the hall.

Suddenly, Patty saw something that gave her a great scare. It was the shadow of a cat, then another shadow and another. Three cats were following Patty's family into the kitchen.

Patty said to herself, "I must do something to save my family." Patty thought for a moment and then snuck through the mouse hole. She went along the edge of the rug and down the hall. She was now behind the three cats, and the three cats were behind Patty's family.

Patty was going to tell her family, "Cats are behind you. Run." But just as she was going to warn the others, she saw shadows on the other side of the kitchen. There were two more cats in front of Patty's family, waiting for them. If the mice started to run, they would run right into the cats who were waiting.

All five cats were slowly moving toward her family. One of the cats behind the mice was getting very close to one of Patty's sisters. That cat was getting ready to pounce.

More to come.

One day, Gorman was walking in the field. He bumped into a scare crow. He said, "I'm sorry, I didn't see you standing there."

A crow was watching Gorman and said to herself, "I'll have some fun with Gorman."

The crow landed on top of the scare crow and said to Gorman, "Why don't you watch where you are going?"

Gorman said, "Well, I . . . I'm sorry. I'll be more careful next time."

The wise old snake saw what the crow was doing and slid over behind the crow. Then the snake talked in the voice of the big one. The snake said, "Oh, shame on you crow, for playing tricks on that goat."

The crow took off and was never seen again.

1. What did Gorman bump into?

2. Did Gorman know that he bumped into a scare crow?

3. Who landed on top of the scare crow?

4. Who talked in the voice of the big one?

5. Did the snake scare the crow?

oy ew oi or aw ce

1. mir**ror**
2. b**ounce**
3. bonk
4. **c**urled
5. n**oi**se

1. circus
2. through
3. **ce**iling
4. knocked
5. watching

1. <u>trapez</u>e
2. <u>backward</u>
3. <u>be</u>hind
4. <u>ex</u>plained
5. <u>loud</u>est

1. cheese
2. brav<u>e</u>
3. flick
4. joy
5. expert

1. p<u>aws</u>
2. claws
3. bl<u>ew</u>
4. flew

Patty and the Cats
Part Four

Patty's family was in the kitchen of the house. Behind them were three cats. In front of them were two more cats. One of the cats was getting ready to pounce on Patty's sister.

Patty tried to think, but her thoughts were mixed up. She just stood there in the dark, watching the cat flick his tail. Now the cat was starting to leap. Patty could see sharp claws on his front paws.

Without thinking, Patty shouted in her loudest voice, "WATCH OUT."

The room shook so hard that two paintings fell off the wall. One cat had planned to jump one foot high and land on Patty's sister. That cat jumped 8 feet high and hit his head against the <u>ce</u>iling. He landed on the kitchen table.

Patty's voice sent the other four cats flying, too.
When those cats landed, they were howling and
running as fast as they could go.

The mice had been knocked into a pile against
the kitchen wall. Slowly they picked themselves up
and went back to their mouse home with Patty.

We are very pr<u>ou</u>d of you.

When the mice were safe inside their home, Patty explained why she had shouted. Everybody in her family looked at her without saying a word. They didn't talk because they couldn't hear anything that Patty said.

Three days later, when the mice could hear again, they gave Patty a cheese party. Her dad said, "We are very pr<u>ou</u>d of you. You are a brave mouse, and you saved us from those cats. Thank you."

Patty had tears in her eyes again. But they were tears of joy. From that day on, Patty went everywhere with her family. They didn't mind Patty's loud voice because they knew they would be safe.

The end.

A man woke up one night. He thought he heard a n<u>oi</u>se. He snuck from his bedroom into the dark hall. When he got to the end of the hall, he looked around the corner. He saw a fa<u>ce</u> looking back at him. The man screamed and turned on the lights.

When the man looked around the corner again, he didn't see anyone. What he saw was a painting of himself hanging on the wall.

The man felt foolish. He said to himself, "I forgot that painting was there. I will remember that painting next time." Then he went back to sleep.

1. The man got up because he thought he heard ▮▮▮.
- a n<u>oi</u>se
- a goat
- Patty

2. The first time the man looked around the corner, what did he see?
- a robber
- a fa<u>ce</u>
- a dog

3. What did the man do?
- ran
- screamed
- fainted

4. The man really saw a painting of ▮▮▮.

5. Do you think the man will remember that painting next time?

1. liar
2. unicycle
3. argue
4. argument
5. known

1. ad
2. noise
3. tent
4. tight
5. riding
6. threw

1. circus
2. trapeze
3. juggle
4. settle
5. newspaper
6. perform

1. Sherlock
2. Moe
3. nothing
4. expert

The Circus
Part One

Sherlock and Moe were known as the bragging rats, but they had not bragged for a year. Their last fight was about which rat could bake the best pie.

A new fight started one spring day. Sherlock and Moe were looking at an ad that was on the ground. The ad was for a circus.

Moe said, "I can do circus tricks better than anybody else in the world. I can walk the tight rope. I can juggle anything. And I am an expert at riding a unicycle."

Sherlock said, "You think you're an expert. I am the expert. I can do tricks on the trapeze that you have never even seen before. I can juggle 12 nuts at once. I can . . . "

"That's nothing," Moe shouted. "I can juggle 40 nuts while I am on a trapeze doing tricks that nobody has ever seen before."

The rats shouted for a long time. The other rats in the pack were getting very tired of the noise and the lies.

At last the wise old rat walked over to the bragging rats and said, "Be quiet. There is a way to settle this. We will have a circus. And then we will see which of you does the best circus tricks."

So all the rats in the pack worked very hard to set up a circus tent with a tight rope, a trapeze, unicycles, and lots of things to juggle. Soon it was time for the bragging rats to show off their circus tricks.

More next time.

Winter was almost over, and Jan was sad. She loved to sled in the snow. She loved to hike in the snow. She just loved snow. But she knew that soon the snow would melt. She said to herself, "I will save some snow so I can have it later." She gathered up large piles of snow and took them to a place where the snow would not melt.

Later that day, Jan's mother came home from the store. She had food to put in the freezer. But when she opened up the freezer, she saw that there was no room for the food. The freezer was filled up with snow. Jan's mom was not very happy. And Jan had to take all that snow out of the freezer.

1. Jan was sad because winter was almost ▮▮▮▮.

2. What did Jan love?
   - snow   - rain   - clouds

3. Where did Jan put her snow?

4. When her mom came home, was there room in the freezer?

5. What did Jan have to do with all the snow that was in the freezer?

ew oy oi aw ge ce

1. carry
2. closed
3. bounce
4. tie
5. people

1. perform
2. expert
3. laughter
4. eaten
5. juggling
6. argue

1. eight
2. eye
3. heard
4. through
5. threw
6. asleep

1. climbed
2. ladder
3. answer
4. shoes
5. clown

Today we will have a contest.

The Circus
Part Two

It was the day of the circus. Moe and Sherlock were still arguing. Moe said, "It's going to be so easy to beat you that I could do it with one eye closed and with one leg tied up."

"Oh yeah?" Sherlock said. "I could beat you while I was asleep with two legs tied up."

All the rats from the pack gathered in the tent. The wise old rat said, "Today we will have a contest of circus tricks. Behind me are the two rats who will perform. You will say which of the rats is the best at doing circus tricks."

The first contest was juggling. Moe started out with four nuts. He threw all four in the air. Two landed on his head. Two landed on the floor. None landed in his paws.

The crowd roared with laughter.

Sherlock started out with four nuts. He threw them into the air. Three nuts hit him on the head. One nut landed on the floor, b<u>oun</u>ce<u>d</u> up, and landed in his paw. He said, "That is what I planned to do."

The crowd laughed.

The wise old rat said, "For the next contest, the rats will ride unicycles."

Both bragging rats tried to ride at the same time. They got on. They ran into each other. They fell down. And they did a lot of yelling at each other. "You knocked me down. Stay out of my way."

The crowd laughed a lot.

This story is not over.

One day, Henry said to himself, "I think I will go for a long walk." So he started to walk. He walked from his house to the other side of town. When he got there, he said, "I think I'll just keep on walking." And that's what he did. He walked all day long. At the end of the day, he said, "I don't want to walk any more." So he stopped right where he was.

He was next to a farm house. After a while, the farmer came out and said, "Why don't you go back home?"

Henry said, "Because I don't want to walk any more."

The farmer said, "Well, then, why don't you run home?"

Henry liked that plan. So he ran home.

1. One day, Henry went for a long ▢▢▢.

2. Did he stop walking when he got to the other side of town?

3. When he finally stopped, he was near a ▢▢▢.

4. Did he want to walk any more?

5. So how did he get home?

1. east
2. west
3. porch
4. change
5. few

1. ladder
2. ouch
3. night
4. snooze
5. yawn
6. flew

1. tightly
2. climbing
3. crawling
4. polite
5. noisy

1. violin
2. sure
3. school
4. shoes

1. spite
2. amaze
3. clown
4. vote

208

The Circus
Part Three

After the bragging rats tried to juggle and ride unicycles, they tried walking the tight rope.

Moe climbed the ladder and was getting ready to go on the tight rope. He looked scared. Then he said, "Oh, I forgot my tight rope shoes. So I can't do it."

As Moe started back down the ladder, he slipped and fell. The crowd laughed.

Sherlock said, "You don't even know how to walk on a tight rope. Watch me."

He climbed the ladder and crawled out on the tight rope. Then he slipped and was hanging by one paw. Then he was yelling and hanging by no paws. Ouch. He landed on the floor, and the crowd laughed.

The last contest was the trapeze. Both the rats tried to get on the same trapeze, but soon both of them were hanging by one paw. Then they were hanging by no paws. Ouch.

The rats in the crowd laughed so loudly that they could not hear the bragging rats yelling at each other. "You got in my way. I was getting ready to do a great trick."

"No, you got in my way."

After the laughter stopped, everybody voted for the rat that did the best circus tricks.

More arguing.
Here we go again.

Did one of the bragging rats win the juggling contest or the unicycle contest? No.

Did one of them win the tight rope contest or the trapeze contest? No.

But all the other rats agreed that the bragging rats won one contest. They were the best clowns anybody had ever seen.

"I know that," Moe said. "Because I'm the best clown in the world."

"No way," Sherlock said. "I got a lot more laughter than you did. People who know good clowns know I am really funny."

The wise old rat said, "More arguing. Here we go again."

This story is over.

A boy loved things that flew. He loved airplanes and birds and kites and balloons. He asked his mother, "Could I be a bird so I can fly?"

His mother said, "You can not be a bird. You are a boy, and boys can't be birds."

The boy said, "But I want to fly."

"You can't fly," his mother said. "But you can fly your kite."

The boy thought flying his kite was a great plan. So he and his mother went to the park and flew his kite.

1. The boy loved things that ███████.

2. The boy asked his mother if he could be a ███████.

3. She told him to fly a ███████.

4. Where did the boy and his mother go to fly a kite?

1. pledge
2. bridge
3. change
4. space
5. dice

1. package
2. milking
3. understand
4. clothespin
5. violin
6. letters

1. Goober
2. porch
3. snooze
4. chew
5. few
6. threw

1. closed
2. beet
3. dot
4. west
5. squeak
6. east

Goober
Part One

There once were two towns, East Town and West Town. Those towns were about two miles apart. Right between the two towns was a farm. And on that farm lived a man everybody called Goober.

That wasn't really his name, but that's what they called him. Everybody knew Goober. If you asked the people who lived in East Town or West Town what they thought about Goober, you would find out that they didn't know how to feel about him. They liked him for some things, and they hated him for other things.

They liked his music. It was sweet and fine. Goober made music with an old violin. You would never know it was old from the lovely sound it made. Goober sat on his porch every summer evening and played his violin. The air would carry that music for miles.

So the people in East Town and West Town would sit outside and listen to the sweet music if the wind was blowing the right way.

But if the wind was not blowing the right way, most people didn't stay outside and listen to the music. They ran inside very fast. And at those times, most people didn't like Goober. Why? Goober's farm had a very bad smell. He had dirty pigs that never took a bath. And their smell was so bad that when the wind was blowing to the east, people in East Town could smell it. Most people would say "phew" and go inside. They would close all the doors and windows—even if the evening was very warm. They would keep their houses closed up until the wind changed and stopped blowing toward East Town.

A few people would stay outside and listen to the music. Those people would put a clothespin over their nose so they could not smell anything. They would listen to the music until after the sun went down. Then they would go inside and take the clothespin off their nose.

More to come.

A dog loved to dig. He found a little mole hole and started to make it bigger. And as the hole got deeper and deeper, the hill of dirt next to the hole got bigger and bigger. Soon that hill was almost as big as a mountain. The dog told his pals, "I made a mountain out of a mole hill."

A mole saw the mountain and said, "This pile of dirt is too big." So the mole started putting the dirt back into the hole. The mountain got smaller and smaller until it was a tiny hill. The mole told his pals, "The dog made a mountain out of a mole hill, but I made a mole hill out of a mountain."

1. Who made a mole hole bigger?
2. The dog told his pals that he made a ▮▮▮▮ out of a ▮▮▮▮.
3. Who put most of the dirt back in the hole?
4. The mole told his pals that he made a ▮▮▮▮ out of a ▮▮▮▮.

A

1. <u>bull</u>dog
2. <u>butter</u>flies
3. <u>snow</u>flakes
4. <u>clothes</u>pin
5. <u>pack</u>age
6. <u>under</u>stand

B

1. di<u>c</u>e
2. lo<u>dg</u>e
3. dan<u>g</u>er
4. golly
5. s<u>ou</u>th
6. stink

C

1. <u>milk</u>ing
2. <u>hold</u>ing
3. <u>scrub</u>bed
4. <u>clean</u>ed
5. <u>smell</u>ing
6. <u>sniff</u>ed

D

1. catch
2. lost
3. track
4. bon<u>e</u>
5. letters

Goober
Part Two

Goober lived on a farm that was right between
two towns. When the wind was blowing to the east,
most of the people in East Town were not very happy.
And when the wind was blowing to the west, most of
the people in West Town were not very happy.

The people were not happy because of the smell
from Goober's farm. But when they ran inside to get
away from the smell, they could not hear the
sweet music. Some people really wanted to hear
the music. Those people stayed outside and put a
clothespin on their nose. But then they didn't like
to talk to each other. They couldn't say words
that had the letters **N** or **M.** They couldn't say the
word **not.** It sounded like **dot.** They couldn't say
the word **meet.** It sounded like **beet.**

The people in East Town and West Town loved it when there was no wind. Then they could all sit outside and listen to Goober's lovely violin music. Some people liked Goober all the time. They lived more than a mile from Goober's farm. The wind would carry the smell from Goober's pigs a mile, but no more. So the smell would not reach people who lived far away. They could listen to the sweet music without having to smell Goober's farm.

Then one summer morning, something very strange happened. A little girl from West Town went over to Goober's farm to visit him. That was strange because nobody ever visited Goober.

The little girl took a big package with her. She walked up to his barn. Goober was milking a cow. Stinky pigs were all around him. The little girl held her nose because the smell was very bad. She tried to say, "Mister Goober, you make nice music."

But she was holding her nose. So here is how it sounded. "Bister Goober, you bake dice busic."

Goober looked up and said, "I do what?"

She said, "Bake dice busic."

He said, "I don't understand. If you would stop holding your nose, I would know what you are trying to say."

More to come.

Kathy liked to go to the forest and look for birds. One day she went into the forest and heard a little tiny bird song. She said to herself, "That bird has a tiny voice, so it must be a tiny bird." She looked up in the trees and saw a tiny yellow bird.

Then she heard a great loud bird song. She said to herself, "That must be a great big bird." She looked up in the trees and all around, but she did not see a great big bird. She saw some black birds and a little tiny red bird. As she was watching the red bird, it opened its little tiny beak and let out a great loud song. Kathy said to herself, "Some birds have a little body, but a big voice."

1. Where did Kathy go to see birds?

2. One day she heard a tiny song and saw a ▇▇▇▇▇ yellow bird.

3. What kind of song did she hear next?

4. Was a big bird or a little bird making that song?

5. What kind of voice do some tiny birds have?

1. stink
2. scrubbed
3. sniffed
4. strange
5. stream

1. <u>wadd</u>le
2. <u>midd</u>le
3. <u>bull</u>dog
4. <u>yaw</u>ning

1. gone
2. wrong
3. h<u>ou</u>rs
4. flat
5. s<u>ou</u>th

1.25

1. lif e
2. track
3. ham
4. bon e
5. rabbit
6. golly

SALE

We love your music, but . . .

Goober
Part Three

A little girl went to visit Goober. She had a package with her. She tried to talk to Goober, but she was holding her nose, and he could not understand what she was trying to say. She tried to say, "You make nice music," but she really said, "You bake dice busic." Goober told her to stop holding her nose so he could understand what she was saying.

So the little girl took in a lot of air. Then she let go of her nose and talked very quickly. She said, "We love your music, but you need to clean up your pigs. They stink." When she was done talking, she grabbed her nose again.

Goober's eyes got wide. He looked at the little girl for a long time. Then he said, "Do my pigs really stink?"

She said, "Yes."

"Golly," he said. "I didn't know that."

She handed Goober her package and said, "Here are sub thigs for you." She turned around and ran away. She was still holding her nose.

Goober opened the package. Inside were some bars of pig soap.

Goober smelled the soap and said, "What a strange smell."

Then Goober went down to the pond with the package. He called his pigs. They came running. Then he jumped into the pond with the pigs and scrubbed them until they were pink. Scrub, scrub, scrub. He rubbed and scrubbed and washed and cleaned. When he was done, his pigs were as clean and sweet smelling as anybody in East Town or West Town. He sniffed the air and said, "Those pigs really smell strange."

Now things are different in West Town and East Town. People sit outside and listen to the music every summer evening. And the air is as sweet as the violin music they listen to. If you go to one of those towns and ask people about Goober, they'll have wonderful things to say about him and his music. And they also have some very nice things to say about a little girl from West Town who goes to visit Goober every week. She always leaves a package with him, and the people in West Town and East Town are very glad that she does.

The end.

Marta didn't like to get dirty, but she wanted to help her mom plant some trees in their yard. She put on her mittens so her hands wouldn't get dirty. She put on her old pants, too. She didn't want to get her nice school pants dirty.

Marta's mom was very dirty from planting trees in the dirt. Her hands were dirty, and her shirt was dirty. There was dirt even in her hair.

Marta went outside to help her mom plant the trees. They watered the plants and patted the dirt around the plants. Marta got mud all over her mittens. When she rubbed her face, she got dirt on her face. Pretty soon, Marta had dirt on her shirt and dirt on her pants. Soon she was as dirty as her mom. But Marta didn't mind. She told her mom, "Sometimes getting dirty is fun."

1. What did Marta want to help her mom do?

2. Marta put on mittens to keep her hands from getting ▩▩▩.

3. Did Marta's mom get dirty?

4. Did Marta get dirty?

5. She said, "Sometimes getting dirty is ▩▩▩."

ew oi ce dge aw

1. Andrea
2. Honey
3. waddle
4. life
5. middle
6. butterflies

1. alarm
2. napping
3. swung
4. hissed
5. net
6. snort

1. nip
2. snip
3. flew
4. threw

1. ski
2. interesting
3. cloth
4. often
5. station

Honey and Sweetie
Part One

There once was the meanest looking bulldog
you ever saw. Her bottom teeth stuck out, and
she looked like she was ready to bite somebody.
People were always shocked to find out that this
bulldog was named Honey.

She got that name because she was as sweet as
honey. She loved people. She loved other dogs.
She even liked some animals you would not think a
dog would like. One of Honey's friends was a
little gray mouse named Andrea.

Honey would sometimes sniff around the house trying to find Andrea. Andrea lived in the hall. She really lived behind a little hole in the hall wall. But in the middle of the day, she could be in a lot of places. So Honey would sniff around and try to find her. Sometimes Honey would find Andrea, and sometimes she wouldn't, because Andrea was very, very shy.

There was only one thing that Honey didn't like. That was cats. She could get along with some cats. But she really didn't like cats that chased birds, butterflies, or mice. She said to herself, "That's not nice."

One day, Honey was napping on the back porch of her house. She woke up when a woman holding a big yellow cat came up the steps. When Honey saw that cat, she said to herself, "Yuk. I hope that thing does not stay around here very long."

The woman and the cat went inside. After a while, Honey got up, yawned, and waddled into the house.

The woman was sitting at the table, but where was the cat? That's what the woman wanted to know, too. She said, "Where did Sweetie go?"

Everybody found out where he was in the next moment. The sounds of running came from the next room. Honey waddled into that room. Then she became very mad. She saw poor little Andrea running for her life. And right behind her was that mean yellow cat. The cat and the mouse shot around the room, this way and that way. They went under the table and across the rug. Then they went into the hall, around a coat stand, and back to the room where Honey was standing.

More next time.

Sammy the goat liked to go for walks. He would walk around the farm every day. He walked around for a very long time. Sammy never got tired of walking.

One day, Sammy wanted to walk to the forest. That forest was very far away. He told the other goats, "I'm going to walk all the way to the forest, and I'm going alone."

"No, don't go alone," the other goats said. "It's too far."

Sammy didn't listen to those goats. So he walked for miles and miles. Pretty soon, it was getting dark, and Sammy still wasn't at the forest. He was starting to get scared.

This is not the end.

1. What did Sammy like to do?

2. Where did Sammy want to walk to?

3. Was the forest near the farm?

4. Did his goat friends think he should go alone?

5. It was getting dark and Sammy was starting to get ▓▓▓▓.

A

1. ski
2. cloth
3. often
4. station
5. waddled

B

1. scraps
2. thick
3. nip
4. hissed
5. howled
6. given

C

1. soup
2. slopes
3. ruff
4. meat
5. net
6. swung

D

1. <u>interesting</u>
2. <u>kennel</u>
3. <u>snorting</u>
4. <u>sticking</u>

Honey and Sweetie
Part Two

Poor little Andrea was being chased by a mean yellow cat. They had run down the hall and back into the room where Honey was standing. Honey was ready to help Andrea out, but before she could do anything, Andrea and Sweetie darted under the table. Sweetie tried to pounce on Andrea, but his claws got stuck on the table cloth. Down came the table cloth. It fell over Sweetie like a big white net.

Sweetie tried to get free. He swung at the table cloth, bit at it, and tried to roll away from it. But the more he tried to fight and roll, the more he was trapped inside that table cloth. Only two parts of Sweetie were sticking out. His yellow tail was sticking out of one end of the table cloth, and his nose was sticking out of the other end.

While Sweetie was rolling around and trying to get free, Andrea darted down the hall and into her hole. She was very scared. Honey looked at Sweetie and said to herself, "It is time to teach this cat a lesson."

She waddled over to Sweetie and gave his tail a little bite. It was not a great bite, just a little nip. "There," Honey said to herself, and waddled outside.

Sweetie howled and hissed and rolled around inside the table cloth. At last, he got free. He looked around the room, but he didn't see Andrea because she was in her mouse hole. And Sweetie didn't see Honey because she was outside. Sweetie didn't know who bit his tail. He never saw Honey in the room, so he didn't even think about her. He said to himself, "The only one who could have given me that big bite was that little tiny mouse."

Sweetie shook his head and said to himself, "That mouse looks really weak, but she can really bite hard."

That was the last time Sweetie ever chased Andrea. In fact, there are a lot of things that Sweetie does not chase. He doesn't chase mice, and he doesn't chase little birds.

The end.

Sammy had been walking for a very long time, and it was getting dark. Sammy was scared to be alone in the dark. He stopped near a stream and said, "I wish my friends were here." Then he said, "I will rest here. I hope no lions or tigers come after me."

Just as he was falling asleep, he heard loud noises. Somebody was coming closer and closer. Sammy was very scared. But just then, he saw who was coming. It was his goat friends. One of them shouted, "Sammy, we couldn't let you go by yourself. We wanted to make sure you were safe."

The next day, Sammy and his pals walked to the forest together.

The end.

1. Sammy was scared to be alone in the ▓▓▓▓▓.

2. Where did Sammy stop and rest?

3. What did he hear in the dark?

4. Who went with him to the forest the next day?

1. often
2. gone
3. wrong
4. lost

1. h<u>ou</u>rs
2. cat<u>ch</u>
3. al<u>arm</u>
4. sn<u>or</u>ting

1. <u>chas</u>ing
2. <u>find</u>ing
3. <u>track</u>ing
4. <u>pick</u>ing
5. <u>act</u>ing

1. climbers
2. snowballs
3. rabbit
4. danger

1. Dud
2. ham
3. slope
4. flat

He's playing in the snow again.

Dot and Dud
Part One

Once there were two big work dogs named Dot and Dud. Dot was Dud's sister. The two dogs lived with five other work dogs at the ranger station high in the mountains. Their job was to find mountain climbers who got lost or hurt. That was their job, but there was one big problem with that job. That problem was Dud. They called him Dud because that's what he was—a big dud at doing his job. When a climber was missing, the ranger would send the dogs to find him. The other dogs would find the climber. Then they would have to find Dud. Dud would get lost. Most of the time, the dog who found the mountain climber was Dot. She was the best dog in all the mountains.

Dud was not good at his job because he didn't like to work. He didn't like to put his nose in the cold snow and sniff for a smell that would lead him to the lost climber. Dud acted like he was tracking through the snow, but he was just acting. While he should have been thinking about finding the lost climber, he was often thinking about eating a large ham bone or sleeping next to the big fire place down at the ranger's station.

Most of the other work dogs would get mad at Dud because they knew he wasn't trying hard. "Come on," they'd say to him. "Stop being such a baby and get to work."

"Okay," Dud would say. "I will. I will." But he didn't.

One time, the other dogs got really mad. Dud had gone out to find a climber, but he got lost. The other dogs spent hours finding him. When they got back to the kennel, the oldest dog said, "While we work, you are out there playing around, running after your tail, rolling snowballs with your nose, or chasing rabbits."

"Yeah," another dog said. "And you don't even know where you are. When we found you, you were less than a mile from the station, and you didn't even know how to get back here."

Dot said, "Stop picking on my brother. He can do this job, and he will work hard. Won't you, Dud?"

"I will. I will," Dud said. "I'll work hard."

Dud was not telling a lie. He had made up his mind to do a good job. But of course, the other dogs didn't believe him.

More next time.

A black eagle lived near a stream. One day that eagle was in a tree when she saw a big fish. She said, "That fish is near a brown rock. So I will swoop down and go right over that rock. Then I will grab that fish."

The eagle swooped down, but her plan didn't work, because the brown rock moved. And she flew right into it. That brown rock was not a rock at all. It was a moose. And the moose was very mad at the eagle.

So now the eagle makes sure there are no big brown rocks in the stream before she swoops down to go fishing.

1. Who wanted to get a fish?

2. Was the eagle red, yellow, or black?

3. The eagle planned to swoop over a ▆▆▆▆▆.

4. What was the brown rock?

5. Was the moose happy or mad?

ge

ew

oi

aw

ce

1. dang**e**r
2. snorting
3. slop**e**s
4. shadow
5. wrong

1. <u>head</u>ed
2. <u>snow</u>ing
3. <u>snooz</u>ing
4. <u>fall</u>ing
5. <u>snow</u>flak**e**s
6. <u>friend</u>ly

1. soup
2. howled
3. rocky
4. reached
5. barked

1. <u>lodge</u>
2. scraps
3. ruff
4. passed
5. meat
6. thick

Dot and Dud
Part Two

The other work dogs were mad at Dud for being a dud. Dud was also mad at himself. He had made up his mind to try harder. That's what he told the others, but they didn't believe him. He had said the same thing many times before.

Just then, the alarm sounded. That told the dogs that a mountain climber was in danger. Three rangers ran to the kennel and let the dogs out. They all headed north to where mountain climbers climb. The dogs sniffed for the trail of the lost climber as they went up higher and higher. Dud even put his nose in the snow a few times and tried very hard to smell something. It was hard work, sniffing and snorting and going up the steep slope.

After a while, Dud began to walk slower and slower. Soon he was far behind the other dogs. Then Dud came to a place that was not steep. It was almost flat. There, Dud did something that was more interesting than sniffing snow. He chased his shadow. Dud jumped up, and the shadow moved. Dud pounced on the shadow. He rolled over on the shadow. He ran around and around, faster and faster, trying to catch that shadow. He even barked at his shadow. This was fun, fun, fun.

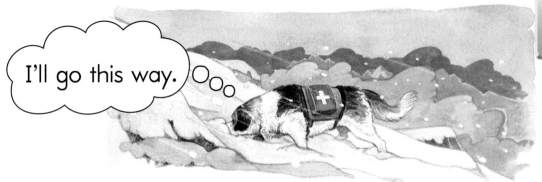

I'll go this way.

Right in the middle of the game, the shadow went away. Dud looked up and saw clouds in the sky. Now it was snowing. Dud couldn't see any of the other dogs. He knew that they were heading north, but he had been running around so much that he didn't know which way north was. He knew that he had to go up a slope, but there were a lot of slopes. Which slope was the right one?

Soon the snow was coming down so hard that Dud couldn't see any slopes—only snow, snow, snow.

Dud looked this way and that way. He tried to sniff the air, but all he could smell were snowflakes. At last he made a choice about which way to go, and his choice was wrong, wrong, wrong. Poor Dud started heading south, not north. He was heading right back toward the ranger station.

More next time.

Little Billy loved to go shopping. One day he said, "Today, I'm going to go shopping for more than I ever shopped for." So Billy went to the big store in the mall. That store had everything. Little Billy got a cart and loaded it with shoes, coats, <u>too</u>ls, food, books, and just about anything else he could reach. Then Billy started to take his things out of the store. A big man stopped him and said, "You have to pay for these things."

Little Billy looked up at the man and said, "Pay? I don't know how to pay."

Just then Billy's mom ran into the store. She said, "I'm sorry for what happened. Little Billy sometimes forgets that he is just three years old."

1. What did Billy like to do?

2. Name two things he put in his cart.

3. Billy had to ▮▮▮ ▮▮▮ the things before he could take them out of the store.

4. What kind of man stopped Billy?

5. How old was Billy?